Westminster Hospital 1716–1974

Dedication

This book is dedicated in gratitude, to all those who have served as Trustees and Governors to the Charitable Society for Relieving the Sick, Poor, and Needy at their Infirmary and Hospital in Westminster from 1720–1974. Their dismissal has gravely diminished the total sum of neighbourly kindliness and goodwill, once the shining glory of the English nation.

Westminster Hospital 1716–1974

J. G. HUMBLE, CVO, FRCP, FRCPath.

Professor of Haematology, London University at Westminster Medical School
Consultant Haematologist, Westminster Hospital
Lecturer in the History of Medicine of the Worshipful Company of Apothecaries
at Westminster Medical School
Student to Westminster since 1931

PETER HANSELL, MRCP, FIIP, Hon. FRPS, FBPA

Director, Department of Photography and Illustration, Westminster Medical School
and Institute of Ophthalmology, University of London
Student to Westminster Medical School from 1941

LONDON: PITMAN MEDICAL PUBLISHING CO

First published 1966
Second edition 1974

SIR ISAAC PITMAN AND SONS LTD
Pitman House, Parker Street, Kingsway,
London WC2B 5PB
P.O. Box 46038, Banda Street, Nairobi, Kenya

SIR ISAAC PITMAN (AUST.) PTY. LTD
Pitman House, 158 Bouverie Street, Carlton,
Victoria 3053, Australia

PITMAN PUBLISHING CORPORATION
6 East 43rd Street, New York, N.Y. 10017, USA

SIR ISAAC PITMAN (CANADA) LTD
495 Wellington Street West, Toronto 135, Canada

THE COPP CLARK PUBLISHING COMPANY
517 Wellington Street West, Toronto 135, Canada

This book has been printed and bound in Great Britain. The text has been set in 10/11pt
Monophoto Baskerville by V. Siviter Smith & Co. Ltd., of Birmingham and printed by
offset lithography by Unwin Brothers of Woking

Preface to Second Edition

When the Chairman of the Board of Governors suggested that a copy of this book should be given to members of the staff on the occasion of the abolition of the Board on April 1st 1974, the Authors took the opportunity to revise the text and increase the illustrations. We hope that those who read it will realise something of the faith of our Founders and the zeal and persistence of those who came after in perpetrating an ideal of service to others that shall be of service to all who follow.

J.G.H.
P.H.

Preface to First Edition

This book is not to be taken as a definitive history of Westminster Hospital; that has still to be written. These meanderings largely arose out of a lecture about our origins given before an audience of 160 magistrates, which met with unaccustomed interest.

Since that time, initiated no doubt by my earlier researches and enquiries, a good deal of additional material has come to light. Thus, with our 250th anniversary in view, many kind friends suggested that the publication of a brief and personal account of our hospital's story would be fitting at this time. I have tried to say something of the origin of the very first Voluntary Hospital and of the men and women who over two-and-a-half centuries have brought it to its present proud position.

It is to be hoped that the illustrations, garnered from many sources and assembled by Peter Hansell, will do something to leaven an unrelieved text and, perhaps, even persuade a few more reluctant readers to turn the pages.

J.G.H.

Acknowledgements

The Authors would like to record their gratitude to the Chairman and the Board of Governors under whose auspices this book has been produced. Thanks are especially due to the Superintendent of the Reading Room of the British Museum and his staff; also to Mr R. A. G. Carson, the Keeper of Coins and Medals. Mr Coyfe of the Department of Prints and Maps has also been most helpful.

Mr Desmond Neill, the Assistant Librarian of the Department of Printed Books, the Bodleian Library, has been most kind. To him we owe the splendid representation of the 'Samaritan Seal' of 1757. Mr L. M. Payne, MBE, FLA, the Librarian of the Royal College of Physicians has been a tower of strength.

Mr E. H. Cornelius, Assistant Librarian, the Royal College of Surgeons, has been another very kind and helpful friend. So, too, have been the Librarian of the Royal Aeronautical Society and Miss Elizabeth Glover, the Archivist of the Worshipful Company of Vintners. Major-General Meneces, CB, CBE, DSO, QHP, MD, FRCP, very kindly gave much assistance on military matters. The late Mr V. H. Clark, Secretary to the Committees, Westminster Hospital, was most helpful. The assistance of Mr Eric Gower, Archivist to the Hospital, was invaluable. To Dr F. D. Hart, MD, FRCP and to Mr R. P. MacMahon, MA, FHA, the House Governor, we owe a special debt of gratitude for reading the manuscript and making many helpful suggestions. We would like to thank Mr K. P. Duguid, FRPS for his expert assistance with the many new illustrations in this Edition, also my secretary Mrs Margaret Brown for her ready assistance. Finally, we wish to thank Mr Whittingham Boothe for his meticulous attention to all the details of publishing this work.

Contents

Illustrations

'In a certain sense all men are historians'
CARLYLE—*Essays*

I

The Beginning

'London, thou art the flower of cities all.'

William Dunbar

At the beginning of the eighteenth century England was at the threshold of that rise to power which over the next two hundred years was to make her pre-eminent among the nations of the world. The sunset glory of the Stuart dynasty came to an end with the death of Queen Anne, and as George I ascended the throne the nation began to take a new account of itself. At this time there were only five and a half million people living in England and Wales, and of these about 674,000 were crammed into London and its environs. London had slowly begun to spread itself, but chiefly to the north and north-west. Westminster, clustering round the Abbey and the old Palace, terminated at Horse-ferry Road; to the west and south-west green marshy fields and ponds stretched down to the reservoirs of the Chelsea Waterworks situated where Victoria Station now is. This area was peculiarly prone to flood-ing, the river bank, in places, being scarcely a foot above the high-tide mark, and the drainage of surface water and sewage was, as a result, problematical. So Kipling wrote of an earlier age—

My privy and well drain into each other
After the custom of Christendie
Fever and fluxes are wasting my mother
Why has the Lord afflicted me?

It is not surprising that the area became notorious for fevers, malaria, typhoid and 'infectious diarrhoea', and that many who had built big houses in the fields deserted them, leaving them to be converted into inns or divided up into the worst kind of lodging house for poor people whose swarming proximity would lead to body lice and, hence, to typhus. The only reason plague disappeared was that the old English black rat *(Rattus rattus)* had been replaced by the brown or Hanoverian rat *(Rattus norwegicus)*. Again, these con-gested dwellings were a perfect setting for tubercu-losis, not only of the lungs but also of skin and of bone, extremely common complaints at this time, and no doubt such conditions were to be found in other parts of London.

Westminster was peculiarly isolated since the city

The Horseferry with Lambeth Palace in the background. (The London Museum)

and central London could be reached only by boat or by passing through Whitehall Palace, a rambling complex which could be approached only through King Street and a narrow gate at the south, progress being barred by yet another gate on the north. The whole area had been devastated by fire in 1698. Passage to the south bank was via the Horseferry, which seems to have been so named because it was the first ferry above London Bridge where horses and horsed vehicles could be transported across the river. It was a lucrative ferry, and belonged to the Archbishop of Canterbury who was paid £3,000 compensation when Westminster Bridge was opened in 1758. The tolls for the ferry, in 1708, were: a man and a horse, 2d.; a horse and chaise, 1s.; a coach and two horses, 1s. 6d.; a coach and four, 2s.; and a coach and six, 2s. 6d.; a laden cart, 2s. 6d.; and a laden wagon, 3s. The ferry had its brief moment in history, for Mary of Modena, with the Old Pretender in her arms, crossed here on 9th/10th December 1668, and on 11th December James II followed, throwing the Great Seal of the Realm into the water near the Lambeth bank.

2

Westminster in the 18th Century. Adapted from Roque's Map 1746.

Strangely enough, the Seal was recovered in a fisherman's net some months later.

Westminster, however, besides being isolated, possessed a still greater disadvantage; it could not have been placed farther away from the only two general hospitals then existent in London. These were, of course, the foundation of St Bartholomew in Smithfield and that of St Thomas in Southwark, which was then where London Bridge station now stands. These institutions were surrendered to Henry VIII in 1540, together with Bethlem (founded in 1271), Christ's Hospital and Bridewell. St Bartholomew's was re-opened (partially endowed) in 1547 but St Thomas's was not re-established until Edward VI was on his deathbed in 1553, changing in the process from St Thomas a Beckett's Hospital to that of St Thomas the Apostle (doubting Thomas), a substitution one would have thought of dubious utility. It seems that Henry VIII did not approve of Thomas a Beckett: 'There was nothing in his life whereby he should be called a Saint, but rather a rebel and Traitor to his Prince'. Since, at that time, imprisonment for debt was customary and the arrangements for parish relief almost non-existent, the position of the sick poor was desperate indeed. Any attempt to relieve the situation would seem, on the face of it, doomed to fail, yet it is a tribute to the basic human virtues of kindliness and compassion that there were found those who would (for no hope of reward) obstinately attempt to improve the lot of these poor wretched sufferers.

On 14th January 1715/16, four men met at St Dunstan's Coffee House, Fleet Street, to do what they could to help the sick poor of London. It is from that momentous meeting that the present Westminster Hospital and Medical School owes its being—as does also, as a curious offshoot from the parent stem, St George's Hospital.

2
The Charitable Proposal

'Mr Hoare said he had ten pounds in his hands.'
Westminster Hospital Minutes, Vol. 1, p. 1,
14th January 1715/16

The four men who met at St Dunstan's Coffee House
in Fleet Street were Mr Henry Hoare, Mr William
Wogan, Mr Witham and the Reverend Patrick
Cockburn. Mr Hoare was a banker, the second son of
Sir Richard Hoare, who had established Hoare's Bank
in Cheapside and, later, in 1690, transferred it to 37
Fleet Street, where it remains to this day. Mr Henry
Hoare in 1716 was 39 years old, a good man and a
devout churchman; Mr Wogan was well known as a
writer on religious subjects; Mr Witham kept the Reg
Tavern in Fleet Street and was a member of the
Worshipful Company of Vintners; and the Reverend
Patrick Cockburn had been curate of St Dunstan's
until 1714, when he was forced to leave because he
was a non-juror.

It is a curious fact that at this meeting minutes were
kept, and this minute book is still the treasured

The Charitable Proposal of 1720.

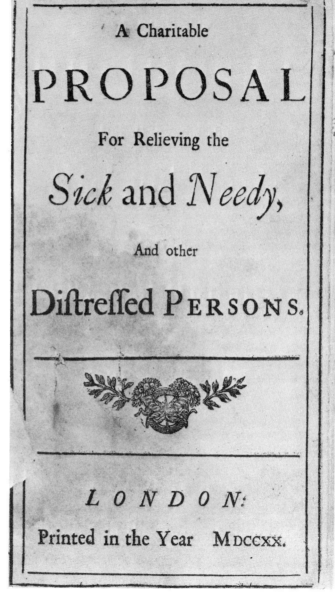

A Charitable

PROPOSAL

For Relieving the

Sick and *Needy,*

And other

Diſtreſſed PERSONS.

LONDON:

Printed in the Year MDCCXX.

Westminster Hospital 1716–1974

property of the hospital; indeed, a complete set of minutes exists, the earlier volumes all written in beautiful and legible handwriting. It would seem certain that the prime mover of this enterprise was Mr Henry Hoare who, at this meeting, reported that 'he had £10 in his hands'. It was decided to distribute this sum among the sick debtors in the London prisons, 'the White Chapple, the Kings Bench, the Clink and the Marshelsea', the task being performed by Mr Witham aided by a Mr Brown.

A striking feature of these early minutes is the 'Charitable Proposal for Relieving the Sick and Needy and Other Distressed Persons'. This is prefixed to the minutes and begins—

'Notwithstanding the provision settled by our laws and the collections made by the charity of well disposed Christians for the relief of the poor, it is obvious to anyone that walks the street that the same is not sufficient to preserve great numbers of them from beggary, to the great grief of all good men and the no small reproach of our religion and country.'

The 'Charitable Proposal' itself appears to have been drawn up by Mr Cockburn (Westminster Hospital Minutes, 14th January 1716, p. 11); it occupies ten pages and includes the 'design' of the Charitable

Mr Henry Hoare: a family portrait at Stourhead. (National Trust and Cortauld's Institute)

The Charitable Proposal

Society, i.e. what they set out to do. It is set out under five headings—

1. 'to provide poor sick people . . .' with necessary food and physick during illness; to procure them the advice of physicians or assistance of surgeons and . . . nurses when necessary, and some charitable women to assist and comfort them and report their condition and wants. If the sick person has a pension from the parish or a right to one, the Society will inform the parish officers and ask for relief for them.
2. 'Many poor, honest women with child are turned out of their lodgings when near their time (when their pains are upon them) and want necessaries during their lying in, whereby they lose their own and infants lives; the Society proposes to provide them with necessaries during lying-in and with nurses if they have no friend or relation.
3. 'Nothing can be more miserable to a poor sick person than confinement in a close unwholesome place (such as prisons commonly are); the Society proposes to visit the prisons and supply sick prisoners with such necessaries as their stock affords.
4. 'Many poor strangers from different parts of the world suffer extreme hardships; the Society proposes to relieve them and help them to return to their native country.
5. 'The Society designs to reclaim the souls of the

The first page of the Westminster Hospital Minutes, 14th January 1715–16.

7

sick . . . . In order to carry out these designs (so goes on the Proposal) it will be necessary to have certain places for repositories for things sent for the relief and supply for the sick, some honest persons to look after them and a messenger to the Society's business. Rich persons are asked to give money and others to send broken victuals, old clothes, linen, beds, bedding, chairs, stools, pots, dishes, glasses & : those of either sex to visit, comfort and read to the sick . . . and solicit subscriptions and physicians, surgeons and apothecaries to give their assistance.'

The Charitable Proposal then gives scriptural warrant for such good works, based on the parable of the Good Samaritan and the exhortatory phrases from St Paul to Timothy, 'laying up for themselves a good foundation against the time to come that they may lay hold on eternal life'.

The minutes record that the four founders were to meet at St Dunstan's Coffee House on Mondays at 5 p.m., and their first regard was to find charitable housekeepers to allot a room as a 'repository' for the use of the sick.

On 1st February Mr Witham reported that he had laid out the £10 in the various prisons on bread, meat and coals, having particular regard for the sick.

On 6th February Mr Hoare paid six guineas, and then a subscription of ten guineas. Mr Witham paid five pounds. It was reported that Elizabeth Cassoon, a leper, was placed in St Barts Hospital—the sum of eighteen shillings necessary for this purpose was allowed.

On 5th March a minute book was to be provided, and another for the names of subscribers. It was reported that Mr Downing had printed 500 copies of the 'Proposal'. The same, stitched in 'Blew paper' would come to thirty-two shillings. Various patients visited are noted (*see* table, p. 9), and a new name, Mr Saville, an apothecary, is noted as a visitor to various patients.

On 12th March Mrs Sherman's name appears; she was a midwife and agreed to receive things given to the Society at her house in Bird Cage Walk.

On 20th March Mr Hoare declined the office of Treasurer and Mr Wogan took on this office, but Mr Hoare paid his subscription of £10 and Mr Witham his £5. Mr Hoare also paid for the 500 copies of the Proposal, and a form of an acknowledgement to be signed by those who were cured by the aid of the Society was drawn up. It read as follows—

I, ... of the Parish of . . . . living in . . . . do hereby acknowledge with a gratefull heart that I did receive relief from ye bounty of ye Charitable Society during . . . . and that by the Blessing of God I am . . . .

3rd April brought a crisis. Mr Wogan proposed : 'that there is an urgent need to admit no more patients and that our principal care be confined to ye sick and needy persons of St Margaret's Parish, Westminster, until it shall please God that our stock increases.' At this meeting, also, a letter was read to the Society from a Dr John Colbatch (actually Sir John Colbatch), who

The Charitable Proposal

Name	Date	Address	Diagnosis	Agent	Form of Relief	Paid
Sick Prisoners	14 Jan.	Various	Sick	Mr Witham	Bread, meat	£10
	1 Feb.	Prisons		Mr Brown	Coals	
Elizabeth Cassoon	5 Mar.	—	Leprosy	—	To St Barts	18s.
Mrs Howell	,,	London Prentice Yd, Minories	Cured	Mr Hoare	—	5s.
Mrs Duncan	,,	A yard nr Press Yd, Newgate	?	Mr Hoare	—	20s.
Mrs Moore	,,	Adama Digging Yd	Pregnant	Mr Wogan	—	6s. 8½d.
Susanna Beaker	,,	George Yard	Pregnant	,,	—	7s. 6d.
A poor woman	,,	?	Fall in street	,,	A plaister	6d.
Mrs Colette*	,,	London Ditch	?	Mr Saville	Visit	—
Phillip Hanna†	,,	Love Court, Shoe Lane	An Asthma	,,	Visit	—
John Bros‡	,,	Sign of the Windmill, Long Ditch	?	,,	Visit	—
Mrs St Leger§	,,	c/o Mr Watts, Charles Court, Strand	?	,,	Visit	—
Ann Prickett	,,	Simple Lane	?	,,	Visit	—
Jane Crookshank	,,	Alms House, Torment Hill	?	,,	Visit	—
Mrs Matt. Matthewson	,,	Sales Cory Street	?	,,	Visit	—
Ann Barker	12 Mar.	?	Syphilis	,,	Salivate, etc.	—
John Bros (2)	,,	Above	?	,,	3 purges	—
Mrs Ogle	,,	St Ann's Lane	Pregnant	Mrs Sherman	Visit	—
Ann Prickett (2)	,,	Above	?	Mr Saville	Pay bakers Bill	11s. 10½d.
Mr Duncan ‖	14 Apr.	Master's Side, Newgate	Sick	,,	Visit	—
Mr Turner	,,	Hudgin Lane, Trinity Lane, Frith St	A dropsy	,,	Visit	—
Ann Boston	,,	?	Dropsy	,,	Reported cured	—
Mrs Cousins	5 May	Tuttle Fields	Dropsy	,,	As above	—
Mary Burton	,,	?	Dang. swelling on throat	,,	Report	—
Mrs Wilds Daughter	,,	?	Scrophulous Distemper	,,	Report	—

Occupation where given:
*Rebecca maker
†Founder
‡Taylor
§Prisoner
‖Clergyman

Total of recorded Subscriptions 30 April–14 Jan. £89 2 0
Total recorded money spent ditto £13 9 7

Personnel of Charitable Society:
Mr Hoare, Mr Witham, Mr Wogan, Mr Cockburn,
Mr Brown, Mrs Sherman, Mr Saville.

was a physician of some notoriety; born in Worcester, he was brought to the notice of George I by his activities in the army, where he claimed to have discovered a haemostatic vulnary and a wound potion (for stopping wounds bleeding and for making them heal). The army finally forbade him to treat any more wounded but George I knighted him none the less.

Sir John wrote to a Mrs Frowde as follows—

Easter Day, 1716.

Good Madam: I have often thought upon that charitable and most Christian scheme that I saw at your house and I shall gladly contribute whatever is in my power to advance it. The City of London has several noble foundations to relieve the needy sick, who are the greatest objects of human compassion; but Westminster, the abode of the Royal family, the premier nobility and gentry of the nation, has no such thing, which is a great reproach to it. Blessed are they that provide for the sick and needy, etc.

I am just delivered from a most dangerous illness, and cannot but seriously reflect with myself, how miserable I had even now been, if I had wanted common necessaries in my distress. Perhaps God laid this on me to engage me in this excellent work. My bowels of compassion have ever been open to the distressed, but what can a slender single fortune do? I am in a good measure able to lay a platform for this excellent work, which I will readily undertake, and promote it by all the ways I am able; as also to be one of the physicians without fee or reward, but what shall redound from the pleasure

and satisfaction of assisting the necessitous.

If you think it proper, pray communicate this to the excellent Society.

I am, etc.

John Colbatch

It was a generous offer from a fashionable physician, whatever his merits, and the Society sent Mr Wogan to wait on him to thank him and request him to be Physician to the Society, a position he was pleased to accept.

Despite the apparent alarm raised by Mr Wogan, the Society continued to meet: on 14th April Mr Saville was requested to buy an alembic and some necessary drugs; Mr Witham said he would pay. Subscriptions continued to come in. Mr Hoare brought £10 from a 'person of quality'; Mr Wogan three guineas from an 'unknown person'. Then came the 5th May: Mr Wogan reported receiving 20 guineas and also 3 guineas from unknown donors; Mr Saville reported on various patients and received payment for the alembic.

And there the minutes end!

No one has yet succeeded in finding any reason why the Charitable Society abandoned its efforts at this point in time. Yet it did, for in the minute book there is a blank page, and the next entry is 2nd December 1719, which begins: 'After long intermission it having pleased Almighty God to revive the Charitable design.' There are, however, some pointers. In 1716, Henry Hoare and Lady Elizabeth Hastings put forward a proposal for a Hospital at Bath to care for the 'Beggars

10

The Charitable Proposal

of Bath'. These were the poor sick people who congregated at Bath to bathe in the warm springs there as a right. This custom had obtained from time immemorial. An Act had been passed in 1714 which abolished this privilege. The 'Beggars' however, continued to arrive for many years and constituted a serious problem, which the proposed hospital was designed to alleviate. Alas, Bath did not open its Hospital until 1742. In 1717, Mr Hoare bought (through trustees, which suggests that his father Sir Richard Hoare was incapacitated) Stourton Manor in Wiltshire. Here, he later, (in 1720) built the present manor house at Stourhead. In 1718, Sir Richard Hoare died. All this suggests a period of considerable difficulty in the Hoare family affairs.

It is, perhaps, also of note that when the 'Charitable Design' was revived, the names of Mr Robert Witham and of Patrick Cockburn are absent. This suggests a possible rift between the four founders as Robert Witham is known to have apprentices bound to him until 30th October 1722, and Spencer says that the family of Patrick Cockburn continued to support the Society at a later date. Fortunately, the original purpose was so powerful in its impact, and the need so great, that Mr Hoare and Mr Wogan were able to revive it at a later date, this time successfully, so that one may truthfully say, *monumentum requiescas, circumspice.*

3
The First Infirmary and Its Origins, 1719–1724

'After long intermission, it having pleased Almighty God...'
Westminster Hospital Minutes, Vol. 1, p. 25,
2nd December 1719

On 2nd December 1719, there met by appointment at St Dunstan's Coffee House twelve men: The Reverend Mr Hutton, Dr Innes, Mr Trebeck, Mr Hayward, Mr Fitzgerald, Mr Wesley, Mr Rupell, Mr Henry Hoare, Mr Wisdome, Mr Russell, Mr Thomson and Mr W. Wogan. They met as 'the Trustees and Managers of the Charity for Relieving the Sick and Needy'.

Of these gentlemen, Mr Thomas Wisdome was a generous Westminster tradesman selling brooms and leather goods. He was also one of the original trustees of the Grey Coat School and Hospital, and became Treasurer, a post he held until 1730. The Reverend Pengrey Hayward succeeded him as Treasurer and held the post from 1730–51. He was a staunch supporter of the Charity and its original ideals. Of the

others, Mr Wesley was Samuel Wesley the Younger, elder brother of John and Charles Wesley, who was at this time a master at Westminster School. In 1733 he became Headmaster at Blundell's School, Tiverton. Mr Trebeck, the Reverend Andrew Trebeck, was the first rector of St George's, Hanover Square.

At this important meeting it was decided to draw up a subscription roll, which had a long preamble beginning—

'Whereas great numbers of poor sick persons in this city languish for want of necessaries and too often die miserably.... We, those names are underwritten, in obedience to the rules of our holy religion, desiring so far as in us lies to find some remedy for this great misery of our poor neighbours, do sub-

12

The First Infirmary, 1719–1724

scribe the following sums of money (during pleasure), by quarterly payments, for the procuring, furnishing and defraying the necessary expenses of an infirmary.'

There were many early subscribers, including Mr Elihu Yate, who said he would be a subscriber until such time as a similar infirmary was built in his parish. One wonders how long he had to wait! At this meeting there occur for the first time the honoured names of Mr William Green and his wife, Mary. One week later a very significant event occurred, for Dr Alexander Stuart promised to be Physician to the Society, the first Consultant to the new foundation. Dr Stuart, who had led a seafaring life until the age of 36, was a graduate of Leyden University. His M.D. Thesis (1711) was entitled *De Structura et Moto Musculorum,* and he was later elected F.R.S. and received the Copley Medal. Until 1733 no man was to work harder to further the interests of the Charitable Society.

The next sixteen meetings from 16th December 1719 to 20th April 1720 were all held at the Grey Coat Hospital, which still stands as it did 250 years ago. If one looks at the steps down to the front of the Grey Coat Hospital (or School, as it is now called), it can be seen how Westminster has literally grown up in the intervening years. These sixteen meetings are largely concerned with subscriptions received, but on 16th December a most important appointment was made, that of Mrs Jane Alden to be Matron. This admirable woman was the perfect choice, generous, kind-hearted

The Grey Coat School. Note the steps down *to the front door.*

and good to her staff, she served the Society faithfully until 1734, when she resigned because of ill health. Her first year's salary was £6 with board and lodging, increased in 1722 to £9 a year (with one guinea gratuity), and in 1725 raised to £12 a year, 'so long as she did not ask for more'. At this meeting also, Sir John Colbatch's name reappears, his services also being accepted. Indeed, on 10th February 1719/20 he informed the Board that Dr Chace and Mr Small (a local surgeon who lived in York Buildings) both offered their services also. Dr Chace is not heard of again, but Mr Small gave good and loyal service. On 10th February, also, Mr Wogan and Mr Wisdome were empowered to look for a suitable house to let to be the new infirmary and, after nearly taking one owned by a Mrs Springale in Broad Sanctuary, the house in Petty France, owned by a Mr Phillips, tallow chandler, was finally leased on 23rd March 1720 at a rent of £22 per annum. It was the second house on the north side in Petty France from its junction with Broadway, now submerged under Queen Anne's Mansions. Mr Phillips generously allowed one quarter's rent free and gave twenty shillings for repairs in the second quarter. On 20th April the Society gave the Grey Coat Hospital two guineas for 'coals and for the children' as a token of thanks for the use of their Boardroom during this time. Ann Miller was hired as a servant to Mrs Alden for £4 a year, and on 20th April the minutes triumphantly announce 'adjourned to Petty France'. By this time (16th March), Dr Stuart had already visited one patient, Mrs Mears—'Dangerous swelling or inflammation in her side'—and

by 23rd March she was improving, a good omen for the success of the Society's venture and its consultant physician.

On 27th April the inscription in 'Gold Letters' was ordered to be fixed to the infirmary—'Infirmary for

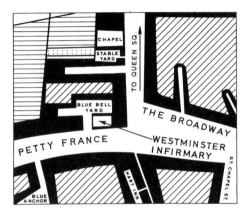

The site of the First Infirmary.
'The tallow chandlers through the blind arch in Petty France'.
(*Pope*)

the Sick and Needy'—and Mrs Green gave one bed and bedstead.

On 4th May Dr Wasey was accepted as the second Physician. He was William Wasey, M.D. (Cantab), later President of the Royal College of Physicians (1750–55). He, too, rendered good and faithful service to the Society until 1733. On 12th May, John Kelly, suffering from 'Evill in the joints and Scurvy' and

14

Infirmary in Petty France

Wednesday 27. Aprill 1720.

Present——

The Rev.ᵈ Dᵈ Innes in the Chair

Mr Hayward.   Mr Wisdom.
Mr Hutton.   Mr Fleetwood.
Mr Trebeck.   Mr Bird.
Mr Fitzgerald.   Mrs Stanton.
                    Mr Wogan.

Dr Innes reported that he had rec'd a Benefaction of Two G.ˢ from Tho. More Esq, and that of Mr More Subscribes two G.ˢ a year from Lady Day.——

Mr Thompson reports that the Lady Harpur Subscribes Three pounds yearly from Lady Day

Resolved that an Inscription in Golden Letters be fixed on the Outside of this Infirmary near the three, in these words

INFIRMARY

For the
SICK and NEEDY.

Mr Wisdom laid before the Bd sev.ˡˡ Bills for necessary bought for ye use of the Infirmary with Receipts from ye Trad.ʲ.men for ye same: order'd that ye payments be allow'd, viz.

recommended by Mr Wogan, was admitted to the infirmary. He was thus the first patient. By 8th June he 'returned thanks to the Society for his cure'. No doubt Dr Stuart's seafaring experience was of considerable help in the management of this case. On 15th June the Grey Coat Hospital gave to the Society, by the hand of the Matron, Mrs Higney (or Hinckney), the following touching gifts of clothes, 'being the work of the Charity Girls'—

20 pair of sheets	4 napkins
24 shifts	6 mens capps
8 towels	4 womens capps
1 tablecloth	14 pr of blankets,
2 dish cloathes	

and an unknown person added 6 mops.

On 24th June Gideon Harvey offered his services (but never attended) and Mr Phillips proffered as Apothecary, but was not satisfactory. He was succeeded on 6th July by Mr Fitzgerald. On 13th July the first account of the working of the infirmary was published. This was a single sheet of paper setting forth the objects of the Society. It gives a résumé of the thirty patients treated from 10th February 1720 to 13th July 1720. There were fourteen out-patients, and sixteen treated as in-patients. Nine were listed cured, one dead, two incurable, twelve were still in the infirmary on 13th July, and there were six out-patients. From the illustration (p.16) one can see that out-patients were seen and patients admitted at the weekly Board meeting on Wednesday evening. Patients were 'ad-

15

Westminster Hospital Minutes for 27th April 1720.

WHEREAS a Charitable PROPOSAL was publifhed in *December* laft for relieving the SICK and NEEDY, by providing them with *Lodging*, with *proper Food* and *Phyfick*, and *Nurfes* to attend them during their Sicknefs, and by procuring them the Advice and Affiftance of *Phyficians* or *Surgeons*, as their Neceffities fhould require ; and by the Bleffing of God upon this Undertaking, fuch Sums of Money have been advanced and fubfcribed by feveral of the Nobility and Gentry of both Sexes, and by fome of the Clergy, as have enabled the Managers of this Charity (who are as many of the Subfcribers as pleafe to be prefent at their weekly Meetings) to carry on in fome meafure what was then

For the Satisfaction of the SUBSCRIBERS and BENEFACTORS, and for animating others to promote and encourage this Pious and Chriftian Work, This is to acquaint them, that in purfuance of the forefaid charitable Propofal, there is an INFIRMARY fet up in *Petty-France, Weft minfter*, where the Poor Sick, who are admitted into it, are attended by *Phyficians*, *Surgeons*, *Apo thecaries* and *Nurfes*, fupplied with *Food* and *Phyfick*, and daily vifited by fome one or other of the CLERGY: At which Place the Society meets every Wednefday Evening for managing and carrying on this Charity, admitting and difcharging Patients, &c.

The following ABSTRACT *will give a fhort Account of the* SICK POOR *that have already come under their Care*.

Names of Patients.	Parifh.	Diftempers.	When receiv'd Out Patients.	When admitted into the Infirmary.	When Cured, Difcharged, &c.
Margaret Collet	St. *Marg. Weftm.*	St. *Anthony's* Fire, aged about 80	10 Febr. 1714.		*Dead.*
Jane Meers	*Ditto*	Ague and Fever	2 March		20 *April* 1720. cured.
Jane Whitaker	*Ditto*	Obftructions	13 *April* 1720.		15 *June* cured.
— *Cowper*, his Wife and 2 Children	*Ditto*	Ague and Fever	20 *April*		1 *May* cured.
Sarah Hill	*Ditto*	Ague and Fever	11 *May*		15 *June* cured
Widow *Harris*	*Ditto*	Sciatica			
John Kelley	*Ditto*	Evil in his Joints, and Scurvy		11 *May* 1720,	8 *June* cured.
Sarah Stevenfon	St. *James's Weftm.*	Scurvy and Palfy	18 *May*	29 *June*	
Ann Phillips	St. *Marg. Weftm.*	Hyfterick Cholick and Headach		18 *May*	
Catherine Cam	St. *Ann's Weftm.*	Afthma and Dropfy		*Ditto*	15 *June* difcharged Incurable
Adrian van Reyney	a Foreigner.	Confumption		25 *May*	8 *June* difcharged Incurable.
Catherine Moor	St. *Marg. Weftm.*	Scorbutick Rheumatifm	1 *June*	15 *June*	
Mary Harris	*Ditto*	Obftructions	*Ditto*	*Ditto*	6 *July* cured.
Ann Robinfon	*Ditto*	Hyfterick Cholick	*Ditto*	*Ditto*	
Thomas Mafon	*Ditto*	A Strain	8 *June*		
Cha. Dunlop, a Child 8 Years old	St. *Mary Savoy.*	A carious Bone in his Knee		15 *June*	
Jane Blackfhaw	St. *Marg. Weftm.*	Dropfy		*Ditto*	
Sarah Stallan	*Ditto*	Scorbutick Rheumatifm, &c.		*Ditto*	
Elifor Davis	*Ditto*	Ague		*Ditto*	
Sarah Whitebead	*Ditto*	A Degree of Leprofy		29 *June*	
Ann Squire, a Child 6 Years old.	*Ditto*	A fcrophulous Cafe		*Ditto*	
Richard Voyce	*Ditto*	Evil in his Head and Knee	29 *June*		
Ann Reeks	*Ditto*	Dropfy	6 *July*		
— *Tight*, a Child of 4 Years old.	*Ditto*	Confumption	*Ditto*		
Nathaniel Harrifon	*Ditto*	Deep Confumption		13 *July*	
William Giddons	*Ditto*	Sciatica and Confumption		*Ditto*	
Elizabeth Dance	*Ditto*	An old intermitting Fever	13 *July*		

Cured ———— 9
Dead ———— 1
Incurable ———— 2
In the Infirmary the 13th of *July*, 1720. } —— 12
Out-Patients ———— 6

In all —— 10

The First Infirmary, 1719–1724

mitted' to the Charity of the Society by means of a recommendation from a Trustee, who was entitled to have one in-patient and one out-patient under treatment at the same time. To be a Trustee one had simply to subscribe two guineas per annum regularly (after 1754 it was raised to three guineas).

On 3rd August we have the first complaint of visitors at unreasonable times: 'ordered that all visitors were to leave at 9 p.m.', and Nurse Squire's wages were raised by one shilling a week.

On 17th September 1720, Robert Winnington, a patient, appeared before the Board accused of, 'behaving in a very rude and scandalous manner and cursing and swearing and complaining of the food'. He offered as a defence that he was drunk, and he was discharged. He was, alas, not the last patient to behave thus, and over the years many patients were discharged for 'irregularity', most of whom were drunk. Indeed, the messenger to the Society, Wm Fenwick, was also discharged on 5th October for 'scandalous and Infamous practices'. There seems to have been a little slackness, for on the same date it was ordered that all out-patients under treatment must appear every Wednesday or send sufficient reason why they could not attend, or they would be discharged.

On 16th November the Trustees sent the following letter to Mr Small, Surgeon, York Buildings—

Sir,

  The astonishing cure you have performed upon Charles Dunlop in saving his Life and Leg, when both were in ye greatest danger, calls for our particular thanks to God, and sincere acknowledgments to yourself for ye same and ye Gent. of this Society do unanimously return you their hearty thanks, hoping you will continue your kind assistance and good office to this Infirmary when it is consonant with your convenience, and they desire you to be assured that they are with great Esteem and Gratitude

Sir, Yr most hum. Servt.
By order of ye Society

16 Nov. 1720   Tho. Wisdome

Charles Dunlop was a little boy of eight, a soldier's son, who had a 'carious bone in the knee', i.e. tuberculosis. He was admitted on 20th May and, after a consultation, the majority were for amputation. Mr Small said he could cure him and succeeded!

In November, Mr Cotes was appointed Apothecary (the third) and his post was renewed again in February 1722.

The New Year brought the first Royal Donation from 'their Royal Highnesses and the young Princesses'. It was £5 5s., a donation from George, Prince of Wales and his wife, Caroline of Ansbach, and their daughters. It may be noted that the Countess of Portland, the Governess to the Royal children, was an early and enthusiastic supporter (and subscriber) to the infirmary. An instance of Mrs Alden's kindness is noted on 21st February when she reported that:

'a man found perishing from cold and hunger in the street had been relieved by giving him victuals, a shirt and 1s. and 6d. to carry him to his home in the country. Resolved, that this being a very extra-ordinary case, the same was allowed and approved by the Board.'

On 19th April the first year's accounts were as follows—

Received	£491	8s.	3d.
Paid out	£417	8s.	3d.
Balance in hand	£73	19s.	9d.

a finding which was, taking everything into account, a very satisfactory one.

On 26th April, David Slack, having been cut for the stone by Mr Douglas, came and gave thanks for his cure. Stone in the urinary bladder was, in those days, and indeed, up to about 1850, a very common condition. Without operation it led inevitably to misery and death. A patient with 'a fit of the stone' could be relieved only by operation, and without anaesthesia this was a hazardous proceeding demanding an opera-tor with nerves of steel and a superb knowledge of anatomy. It is only about this time that the latter need was becoming fulfilled. Mr Douglas, John Douglas, was the surgeon brother of James Douglas the anatomist, still known by his description of the fold of the peritoneum between the bladder and the rectum—the 'pouch of Douglas'. James Douglas had studied the anatomy of the bladder and demonstrated to his brother that when the bladder was distended it rose above the pubis, pushing the peritoneum away behind it. John Douglas then proceeded to operate on four boys with the stone by filling the bladder with water, pushing the stone forwards with the fingers of the left hand in the rectum, and cutting down on the stone above the pubis (in the lower part of the abdomen). He could then pick out the stone through the incision. Three of the four boys recovered and were shown to the Royal Society, and John Douglas was elected F.R.S. in January 1722. In 1723 he was given the Freedom of the Barber-Surgeons Company, and in 1724 he was made a Freeman of the City of London. The four cases are described in his book *Lithotomia Douglasiana* (1723) dedicated to the Trustees and Medical staff of the Westminster Infirmary. This operation was called the 'high apparatus' as distinct from the common methods of lithotomy through the perineum. Many surgeons attempted this technique, including the great Mr Cheselden, but it was found that it very often produced complications and was abandoned in favour of the methods introduced by Cheselden, whose last variation, the 'lateral operation', became the standard. Unfor-tunately, in consequence of this Douglas became em-bittered, and although there was no cause, became Cheselden's most bitter enemy, especially when the latter became attached to the infirmary in 1724. Such then was the first consultant surgeon to the infirmary. Indeed, at the time, his assistance must have been very useful to the Trustees.

In May (the 24th to be exact) an event of apparent small importance but of considerable consequence occurred. Mr Innes brought to a Board meeting the gift, by an unknown lady, of a Broadpiece (i.e. a gold coin of the reign of James I, sometimes called a 'laurel') worth £1 3s., 'and when there is found an object of

A 'Broadpiece' or 'Laurel'. (British Museum)

any poor person that shall be in want of something to put him into the world when discharged from the Infirmary, the same person informed Mr Innes that there was a further £1 3s. to be called for that use'. From this gift there sprang the Samaritan Fund, which was utilised for this purpose for many years. A project in October, which came to nothing, was a petition by Dr Innes to George I on behalf of the infirmary—it was in English, but there was no reply; it was repeated in French, there was still no reply. (Perhaps they should have tried German!).

On 21st November Mr Douglas formally offered his services to the infirmary and they were gratefully accepted, but earlier, on the 8th, Mr Claudius Amyand, F.R.S., Sergeant-Surgeon to George I, also profferred his services. Mr Amyand was of Huguenot extraction, from Mornac Xaintongue, his father Isaac having been naturalised on 10th October 1688. Claudius was admitted to the Barber-Surgeons in 1728 and became Master in 1731. He was an extremely competent surgeon and recorded many cases in the *Philosophical Transactions*. Thus, of the four consultants appointed after 1720, three were Fellows of the Royal Society.

The infirmary affairs continued in their parochial way. There was a complaint that the medicines were too expensive (there still is) and it was investigated. The Bishop of Rochester, Francis Atterbury, who had proclaimed James II after the death of Queen Anne, was approached about a promise he had made to give a piece of land in Tuthill fields (Rochester Row) for the infirmary, but his reply was that times had changed, and not even Mr Henry Hoare could get him to alter his decision. An Order forbidding in-patients to be out after 9 o'clock at night was passed (they were allowed out for only two hours a day). Then, on 20th December 1721, another consultant was invited to join, Ambrose Dickens (or Dickins), the other Sergeant-Surgeon to George I, who came from East Meon in Hampshire. He, too, became Master of the Barber-Surgeons in 1729, but he was not as talented as Amyand. Spurred on by these appointments Douglas persuaded the Trustees to insert the following advertisement in the papers at the charge of the said Mr Douglas—

(7th March 1722)
'Notice is hereby given to the poor troubled with the stone in the bladder that they will be received at the Infirmary in Petty France, Westminster, in order to their cure at all seasons of the year, without any other recommendation than a certificate under the hand of Mr John Douglas, Surgeon, in Fetter Lane, Lithotomist to the said Infirmary.'
'N.B. That Mr Douglas engages to be at the sole charge of cutting and curing all such persons as shall by him be so recommended for the term of two years from that date thereof.'

Whether this advertisement produced any results is not known, but a publication of greater interest was made by the Board in early 1722. It was the 'Proceedings of the Trustees of the Charitable Society for relieving the Sick, Poor and Needy at the Infirmary in Petty France, Westminster'. This took the form of a folded single sheet of paper, thus presenting four sides, on which were set out succinctly the history and aims of the Society. There is a balance sheet also. It would seem that these were given to people intending to become subscribers. The 'Proceedings' also had attached to it a brief account of the people who had been under the care of the Society—

The Following
ABSTRACT
contains An
Account of the Sick-Poor
That have come under their care

From
10*th February* 1719/20–3*rd January* 1721/22

Cured	154
Dead	17
Incurable	22
Discharged for Non-attendance most of 'em supposed, cured	47
Discharged for irregularity	2
Besides advise given in the Infirmary most of whom are cured	69
Total	333

Out patients 6 ⎫
In patients 15 ⎬ 3rd January 1721/22.

An Abstract of the Proceedings of the Trustees of the Charitable Society for relieving the Sick and Needy, etc.

Year	1722	1723	1732	1735	1742	1752	1757
Total from Dec. 1719	333	582	3,116	4,053	—	35,577	45,609
Cured	154	143	249	151	499	1,162	1,520
Dead	17	7	39	37	71	63	53
Incurable	22	17	37	—	—	—	—
Discharged (non-attendance)	47	19	77	116	444	724	623
Discharged (irregularity)	2	4	16	3	4	10	16
Advice given gratis	69	62	87	—	—	—	—
Beds	12	15	31	35	86	83	98

There follows an itemised list of the in-patients' and out-patients' names, their parish, their ailments and their date of discharge. This list of ordinary people possesses a peculiar poignancy of its own. It is impossible to read it without being moved at heart.

These 'Proceedings' were published and distributed annually until 1800, but few have survived outside the Hospital archives. They constitute a unique record of the progress of the institution. In 1720, for instance, the accounts show that £491 8s. 3d. had been received

The First Infirmary, 1719–1724

and £417 8s. 6d. had been spent, leaving a balance of £73 19s. 9d. In 1800 the income was £1,757 16s. and the amount spent was £2,000 11s. 4d. In 1720 there were but two physicians. In 1800 there were three physicians and three surgeons, two of whom, William Lynn and Anthony Carlisle, were old students of the Hospital.

The year 1722 passed uneventfully from April to December, when the infirmary received its first legacy under the will of Isobel, Lady Dod (or Dodd), the widow of the late Lord Chief Baron. It was of £42.

9th January 1722/23 has two interesting (and contrasting) minutes. One is—

'The Physicians Report
That the Patients are in a fair way of recovery.'

Variant of the Samaritan Seal from 'The Proceedings' of 1748.

The second minute:
'Ordered that Mr Wisdome have power to treat about taking the next House to be added to what we at present have.'

Taken together, they can only mean that the Trustees (and the staff) were now confident in the success of their venture and ready to increase the scope of their efforts. They did not, however, succeed in renting the house next door, and no more is heard of this project. An unusual donation on 16th January, from Mr Edmund Fitzgerald, was of 'a Rheam of paper and 100 pens'. On the same day £11 was given to buy 100 copies of the *Christian Monitor*. The financial year closed satisfactorily—receipts £457 1s. 9d., outgoings £392 15s. 9d.

The year 1723 seems, in the main, to have been uneventful except for a bricklayer's bill for £3, which indicates considerable work. In March 1724, Mr Wisdome and Mr Bird without much apparent difficulty secured the rent of new premises from Midsummer at a rent of £35. This house was in 'Chapell Street' which was situated off the east side of Great Chapel Street, the house itself being the seventh south of Dacre Street and the eighth north of Orchard Street. It was thus not far from the first infirmary and was where the new buildings on the north side of Broadway now stand (New Scotland Yard).

The house was owned by John Nicholls, and the lease permitted him and his wife to keep the front parlour, the room behind and the two small cellars under them. They were also to have access to the kitchen and to the warehouse! In return, the house was to be put into tenantable repair 'wind tite and water tite' and the front entrance to be whitewashed. The lease speaks of the house and gardens, thus it must have been much larger than the one in Petty France. The arrangements went smoothly except that Mrs Nicholls insisted on an indemnity by the Trustees in respect of any damages incurred by the premises being used as an infirmary. This was agreed to, and they moved from Petty France to Chapel Street on 10th June 1724. While all these exciting things were going on an apparently trivial incident occurred which had far-reaching consequences. '20th May 1724. Mr. Cheselden and Dr Wasey recommended Thomas Stevens, a stranger, to be cut for the stone. Admitted as Outpatient for a month and Mr Cheselden is desired to perform the operation.' The operation was duly performed satisfactorily and, thus, Mr Cheselden took the place of John Douglas as lithotomist to the infirmary.

A fitting ending to this chapter is the 1720–1724 'Orders for Inpatients'.

'Orders for the Inpatients'
1. No patient to be out above 2 hours without leave.
2. No Inpatients of this Infirmary to be abroad after nine of ye clock.
3. All Visitors to ye Inpatients to leave ye House by nine of ye clock and none to be admitted after that hour unless on Extraordinary Occasions.
4. Ordered that: No person be admitted to visit any of ye Patients in this Infirmary on Sunday till Divine Service is over in ye afternoon and that the Matron take strict care that no strong Liquor be brought into this Infirmary from any Publick House. And that all be obliged to quit ye House by Eight of the Clock.
5. Every One Discharged Cured from this Infirmary be enjoined by the Chairman to give Publick Thanks in their Parish Churches.'

It is nice to think that in the first Book of Orders relating to the affairs of the Infirmary, these regulations are headed—

As to the Servants and Family in General.

4
The Second Infirmary, 1724–1733

'Adjourned to the New House in Chappell Street.'
Westminster Hospital Minutes, Vol. 1, p. 419,
10th June 1724

When the Charitable Society met for the first time in Chapel Street the minutes are continued in a new book most appropriately, and they seem to carry a new spirit in them. Some aspects of this 'new look' seem very foreign to the aims and aspirations that prompted the formation of the Charitable Society.

At their first meeting on 17th June 1724, Mr Cheselden attended and brought £50 from an anonymous donor. The Board wrote out a letter of hearty thanks which they desired Mr Cheselden to give to the unknown benefactor and Mr Cheselden was asked to become Surgeon to the Infirmary. Later writers have not hesitated to imply that the anonymous donor was, in fact, Mr Cheselden himself.

William Cheselden was born on the 19th of October 1688 in Somerby Parish at Burrough on the Hill, Leicestershire. He was the second son of George and Deborah Cheselden and came of an old family entitled to call themselves formally, Gentleman. Wyggeston

School claims William as one of their most illustrious Old Boys. After his apprenticeship to Mr Ferne (*see* Chapter 9) and his early years as a lecturer in Anatomy, he married Deborah Knight, the niece of Robert Knight, the cashier of the South Sea Stock. This was in 1713. In 1714 he bought £1,000 worth of the South Sea Stock and apparently was shrewd enough to dispose of it before the great crash occurred. The Cheseldens had one daughter, Wilhemina, who later married Dr Cotes, who became Physician to the Infirmary in 1732. Cheselden became, first, Assistant Surgeon and, later, full Surgeon to St Thomas's Hospital in 1718–19. He was elected F.R.S. in 1713, and in the 1720s was one of the most talked about and well-known surgeons in England. He was a friend of Alexander Pope whom he advised as to his health. Pope wrote—

'I'll do what Mead and Cheselden advise
To keep these limbs and to preserve these eyes.'

23

Mr William Cheselden, F.R.S., Surgeon to Westminster 1724–39.

Mead, Richard Mead, the grave and courteous Richard Mead, was the foremost physician of the day, and Cheselden's friend.

Cheselden became known as an eye surgeon as well as a lithotomist. He was expert in 'couching' cataracts, and designed and performed an operation for making an artificial pupil, thus bringing sight to certain patients otherwise condemned to a life of blindness. He was an eager, active, impulsive man, quick in perception and speedy in decision. Although generally of a happy and good-natured disposition, he was really sensitive at heart and became pale and nervous before operating. It is said that a French surgeon who had come to see him perform his operation for the stone noted this and commented on it. After the operation Cheselden took him to a boxing match (he being fond of sport), whereupon Mr Cheselden was noted to be at his ease and the Frenchman pale, sweating and nauseated. It may be asked how good a surgeon was he? Many witnesses record that he could extract a stone from the bladder within one minute from the first incision, and a happy victim wrote—

> 'The work was in a moment done
> If possible, without a groan
> So swift thy hand, I could not feel
> The progress of the cutting steel.'

He recorded the results of 213 'stone' cases as shown in the table opposite; they speak for themselves.

The Trustees must have been pleased that he had joined them, but a week later, on the 24th June, there is evidence of a jarring discord within the ranks of the

24

The Second Infirmary, 1724–1733

The lateral operation

Total number of cases   213

Of the first	50,	3 died
Of the second	50,	3 died
Of the third	50,	8 died
Of the remaining	63,	6 died
Total	213,	20 died (9·4%)

Mortality by age groups

Under the age of 10	105 cases	3 died
Between the ages of 10–20	62 cases	4 died
Between the ages of 20–30	12 cases	3 died
Between the ages of 30–40	10 cases	2 died
Between the ages of 40–50	10 cases	2 died
Between the ages of 50–60	7 cases	4 died
Between the ages of 60–70	5 cases	1 died
Between the ages of 70–80	2 cases	1 died

The three largest stones removed in this series weighed 12 oz, 10¼ oz and 8 oz. The largest number of stones removed from one patient was 33.

staff. Dr Wasey was requested to return the book containing the prescriptions given to various patients in the infirmary as it was the property of the infirmary, and the Board passed the following resolution: 'Resolved that Dr Stuart is the Senior Physician to this Infirmary.' This must have been somewhat galling to Dr Wasey. At this meeting, in fact, the only cheerful

note is that Thomas Stephens, cut for the stone three weeks since by Mr Cheselden, gave thanks for his cure and was discharged. It would seem that there was some underground discontent, for one week later, 1st July 1724, the chair at the weekly Board was taken by Mr Henry Hoare and all passed off peacefully, there being no minute suggesting any upset whatsoever. This was the only time that Mr Hoare had ever taken the chair at these meetings since the infirmary was founded. One week later, however, a resolution was passed that there should be four Quarterly Board Meetings on Wednesday after each Quarter Day, 'wherein the Proceedings of the last Quarter should be considered and Approved'.

The following list of salaries and wages also reveals a new feature of the infirmary, namely, a salaried resident surgeon in ordinary, Mr Wilky (or Wilkie).

Salary and wages—8th July 1724

Mr Wilky	Quarterly Salary	£5 0s. 0d.
Mrs Aldin	ditto	£2 5s. 0d.
Edm. Edmonds, messenger	ditto	£1 10s. 0d.
(The Nurse), Marg. Black	ditto	£1 12s. 6d.
(The Maid), Jane Williams	ditto	£1 5s. 0d.

At a later date this appointment of a paid surgeon was commented on as something carried through by a powerful minority, even though opposed to the spirit by which the Society was founded. As a reminder that

WESTMINSTER INFIRMARY IN CHAPELL STREET

A list of the staff during the period 1724–32 with their dates of appointment

Physicians			*Matron*	
Dr Alexander Stuart, FRS,			Mrs Jane Alden	16th December 1719
MD (Leyden)	9th December 1719			
Dr William Wasey,			*Nurse*	
MD (Cantab)	4th May 1720		Nurse Margaret Black	28th February 1722
Dr Richard Holland, FRS	12th August 1724			
Dr George Lewis Tessier, FRS,			*Apothecary*	
MD (Leyden)	14th April 1725		Mr Cotes	30th November 1720
Dr Ross	22nd October 1729			
Surgeons			*Treasurer*	
Mr Sergeant-Surgeon Claudius			Mr Thomas Wisdome	16th December 1719
Amyand, FRS	8th November 1721			
Mr Sergeant-Surgeon Ambrose			*Messenger*	
Dickens	20th December 1721		Edmund Edmunds	4th October 1721
Mr William Cheselden, FRS	17th June 1724			
Resident Surgeon			*Maid*	
Mr Wilkie	17th June 1724		Miss Jane William	1st June 1720

they were not yet done with the early foundation, next week appeared a Mr John Blagden, Surgeon, with a letter of attorney for Mrs Eleanor Bise, the landlady of the house in Petty France demanding £9 8s. for rent due. The Board paid. However, in December they received the sum of one pound 'for old things left in the house in Petty France'. A curious note is that the original first in-patient, John Kelly, returned with sciatica and was admitted as an out-patient on 12th August. Indeed, matters passed relatively peacefully for the rest of the year and the first Quarter of 1725, when the annual accounting showed that £578 9s. 2½d. had been raised and that £419 8s. 10d. had been spent, leaving a balance of £159. This must, indeed, have

26

The Second Infirmary, 1724–1733

been a most satisfactory year's balance. Yet the Charitable Society had suffered a loss on 12th March 1725 to which there is no mention whatsoever in the minutes. For on that date 'at his house in Fleet Street' there died Mr Henry Hoare. He was only 48. That there is no mention in the minutes of this sad event is most surprising, for it was generally agreed that he was the principal force in the founding of the Charitable Society and without whose efforts the infirmary would never have been founded. Let it be remembered for ever of this truly great man that, as it says on his monument in Stourton Church, in which vicinity at Stourhead he had built himself a house: 'He lived under a settled habit of Private Charity and bore a Noble Share in all those Public acts of Piety and Mercy which have continued the Blessings and averted the Judgements of God.'

Besides his efforts in connexion with the infirmary he was a Trustee of the Grey Coat Hospital and was, for many years, Chairman of the Grand Committee of Charity Schools within the Bills of Mortality (of the City of London). He was also a very active founder member of the Society for the Propagation of Christian Knowledge.

In his Will dated 1722/23 (9th February) and in its various codicils dated 1724, he left several sums for charitable bequests, including £100 to St Bartholomew's Hospital, but nothing to the Westminster Infirmary. Why this is so we do not know, but it is possible that he would have altered his Will at a later date. His son, another Henry, was not so active in the affairs of the infirmary, and the close connexion with

The Henry Hoare Monument, Stourton Church.

the Hoare family lapsed until 1775, when they became the hospital bankers. Even today they still handle a small number of old subscriptions to the hospital.

The next event of some note is the accession of yet another physician to the staff on 14th April 1725. This was George Lewis Tessier, F.R.S., M.D. (Leyden) who was Physician to the Household of George I and later Physician in Ordinary to George II. It is noted at this time that the physicians' reports concerning patients are given separately. Apparently they were, as we say at the present time, 'holding their own out-patients'. It is somewhat surprising to find the Trustees (on 19th May) carrying out a rather peculiar financial arrangement. Mr Wilkie applied for permission to take as apprentice a young man—Maurice Manning. The sum asked was £45 and the Trustees were to have two-thirds of this, i.e. £30. This was agreed to and the receipt of the money was duly noted. The summer passed, and on 13th October 1725 Mrs Alden received her last advance of salary to £12 per year, 'On her promise to desire no further advance any more'. As 1726 dawned, Mr Cotes was yet again desired to continue as apothecary, but in March 1726 a major crisis occurred, Mrs Alden having reported on the inferior quality of the beer supplied! The Board conferred and the brewer was changed to Mr Green, at the Matron's request. At the end of March the Board made a resolution to dine at the 'Bell Inn' to consider the 'Accompts', and after this first dinner it is pleasant to read that affairs were once again satisfactory. Income £734 6s. 4d., outgoings £442 5s. 10d., a balance of £292 0s. 6d.

In July there is evidence of the conscientious manner in which the physicians conducted themselves in the affairs of the infirmary. Dr Wasey, desiring a country holiday, introduced Dr Wood to act (unpaid, of course) as his locum tenens for this period, a precedent that has been followed ever since. In August, the number of physicians was increased again by the addition to the staff of Richard Hollond, F.R.S., an indication of the increased work they were doing. Dr Hollond served the infirmary diligently until he died in 1730. In 1728 he published *Observations on Smallpox* which, if it contained nothing new, at least showed a keen interest in what was then a common and deadly disease. The New Year brought gifts to the Matron, the nurse, the servant, the messenger and the apprentice (he was given five shillings) and introduces on the scene Captain Joseph Hudson, who became a subscriber. He was to play a very prominent part in the infirmary affairs later. In March an agreement was satisfactorily concluded with 'Mr J. Nicholls, landlord' to take the whole house for £38 per year clear of all taxes. The infirmary was to maintain 'the two Pumps, two Cisterns, Kitchin Grate and Jack in good order.... He paying the King's Tax and keeping the House in Repair.' This arrangement enabled the Trustees to increase the number of beds, six new beds being purchased in April. In 1726 and 1727 there were eighteen, in 1728 twenty-five and, in 1730, thirty. The further consequence of this was an increase of costs which was not foreseen by the Trustees, who were forced to adopt severe economies in 1729. Meanwhile, the accounts for 1727 were satisfactory, 'charge £844 14s. 9½d.,

28

discharge £504 1s. 9¾d.' The increase of accommodation necessitated some bricklaying, for the bricklayer gave his services, £3 14s. worth, to the infirmary; this proof of generosity among those not well off is a common feature of the minutes. It is in this year that the Lord Bishop of Winchester, Richard Willis, D.D., paid his first subscription—he later became the first President of the infirmary and a focus for a powerful and dissident minority of subscribers bent on their own way. The rest of 1727 and the greater part of 1728 seems to have been relatively uneventful. The yearly accounts, charge £821 16s. 1¾d., discharge £643 9s., were apparently satisfactory. Another event is the appointment of Mr Thomas Hope, oculist, who, introduced by Dr Stuart, offered his services to the infirmary *gratis*. He does not appear to have been very active in the infirmary affairs. The rumblings of financial troubles are shown in January 1729, when it was found necessary to send the following circular letter to the many subscribers who were behind in their subscriptions—

'The Charitable Society for the Sick and Needy in the Infirmary whereof you are a member do hereby give notice that this being the time of the year for making their General Collection of the Subscriptions due, their Messenger will wait upon you in a few days with the Treasurers Recpt for the Arrears of your Subscription from . . . .'

Three hundred copies were ordered to be printed, which argues that this was a most serious state of affairs. A further Royal donation from 'Their Royal High-nesses the Princesses', of £10 10s. was brought by Dr Tessier. This showed that George II (who succeeded in 1727) and Queen Caroline had not forgotten the infirmary, and their interest continued for many years to come. Despite this, the annual audit was disquieting: charge £775 0s. 1d., discharge £580 10s. 7d. The Messenger, the worthy Mr Edmunds, applied to the Board for a relief of some of his duties (he had just got his contract renewed). He requested that, 'James Huxley, In-patient, continued to go of errands, that he (Edmunds) may be allowed a Porter to beat at the Mortar', which was agreed to, and the said James Huxley returned 'Thanks at the same time for his cure'. This was no time for concessions, for in July the Churchwardens of the Parish refused to bury patients free any longer and it was 'ordered that Twenty one shillings be deposited in the Matron's hands before every Patient be received into the House'. A little later, owing to what is described as the low state of the infirmary, all admittances of in-patients and out-patients were stopped until a General Board held on 26th November 1729, when several drastic orders were made—

1. The rule prohibiting an in-patient stay of more than two months was to be enforced.
2. Margaret Black, the nurse, was to be immediately discharged for disobedience to the Matron and not to be allowed to enter the infirmary premises again.
3. Elizabeth Roberts, the servant (who had taken Jane Williams's place in April) to be discharged also, 'not a proper servant to this Infirmary'.

4. Ordinary subscribers were to be limited to two patients only, but the physicians and surgeons were allowed two in-patients and two out-patients each.

5. As a method of raising money it was decided that a sermon should be preached. The Reverend Mr Trebeck was to be approached and the event advertised in the newspapers. Further troubles fell on the Trustees a week later, for Mr Thomas Wisdome, the Treasurer, died. He had served the Society most conscientiously and well and his loss was deeply felt. A new nurse, Elizabeth Hatfield, and a new maid, Mary Bradshaw, were engaged upon a month's trial, 'upon dislike of either' as their contracts said, from 31st December 1729.

On 7th January 1730, Mr Pengrey Hayward was unanimously elected Treasurer, to be assisted by Captain Hudson. The Sermon was to be preached by the Lord Bishop of Winchester. Trustees were appointed to 'desire Mr Trebeck the use of his pulpit on the occasion on the same day in the afternoon'. What Mr Trebeck said to this is not recorded! The next item of the minutes is the report of the first special committee meeting ever held by the Trustees, at Sergeant-Surgeon Amyand's instigation, to reduce the expenses of the infirmary (5th January 1730). The recommendations of this committee, all of which were adopted, were as follows—

1. Edmund Edmunds, the messenger, was to be discharged on Lady Day, 'and to have the thanks of the Society for his faithfull services during the time of his being a servant thereof'.

2. The lad James (Huxley) to be discharged immediately.

3. Any servant carrying victuals out of the House to be discharged immediately.

4. No medicines to be carried out of the House except by out-patients and no fresh medicines to be supplied to them unless the pots and glasses were returned.

5. The Matron was empowered to oblige such in-patients as were able, to assist in nursing, 'washing the linnen and ironing the same', washing the wards and assisting the other patients. Any patient who refused to co-operate was to be expelled.

6. One pound only of beef or mutton was to be allowed for each in-patient per day and only for four days each week. The Matron was to buy only beef with the least bone, and the mutton was to be hind-quarter. The amount of meat ordered each week was not to exceed the numbers of patients allowed meat. One loaf of bread of 16-oz, and three pints of small beer were allowed to each patient per day, except those on a milk diet who were to have three pints of milk and a 16-oz loaf per day. Roots in season (without butter) were to be served (boiled) with the meat. On the other three days the patients were to have: milk porridge, good burgos milk thickened with flour, frumenty, rice milk, pease porridge, suet pudding, 'Dumplins' or sugar sops. (Such a

Patients' pewter porringers, c.1700, now in the possession of Dr F. M. Allchin, given to him by his uncle Sir William Allchin.

quantity as shall not exceed two-thirds of the expense of the flesh days.) Each Servant of the House to have 1 lb of meat per diem and as much bread and beer as the patients.

7. The Trustees were advised to consider whether the Society should be Incorporated and a Charter should be obtained. It was pointed out that this would make it easier to obtain legacies. A note here in support of this states that St Thomas's Hospital had an annual income of £1,800, their outgoings were £3,000, the deficit being met by donations from the Governors and receipt of legacies.

These stern measures were most effective (the meat days were to be Sunday, Tuesday, Thursday and Saturday).

At the end of January the Executors of the late Mr Wisdome handed over the infirmary's assets to the new treasurers, and included in the list is 'the Messenger's Silver Badge (or Ticket)'. It is evident that great concern had been taken over the financial position and

31

The Iron Chest, presented by Sir Brownlow Sherrard 29th March 1732. On top (left) a copy of the 'Charitable Proposal', (right) Vol.1 Westminster Hospital Minutes.

that subscriptions had increased; even Their Royal Highnesses increased their subscription to £31 10s. The financial position had improved: charge £960 11s. 8d., discharge £698 12s. 7d. The saddest note is the discharge of Edmund Edmunds (after ten years), who 'returned thanks for the benefits and civilities he received during his ten years service'. The minutes now contain very many references to the Charter of Incorporation, which never eventuated. The preparation of this was under the guidance of Dr Stuart. The position of the Bishop of Winchester is interesting— without fail he advised them that the time was not ripe, for different reasons each time! However, the Trustees having set their house in order proceeded with their day-to-day affairs. Mr Wilkie's salary was raised £10 per annum. Thomas Clarke (a baker's son) was bound apprentice to the infirmary for £100 plus five

guineas to the Stamp Office to register his indentures. Mary Emberton was engaged servant at £5 per year, and Elizabeth Hatfield, nurse, was discharged sick. She had an ulcer on her leg and was admitted as an in-patient. Elizabeth Nelson took her place at a higher salary, £6 10s. per year.

The year 1731 opened quietly and the accounts really show the effects of the economies: charge £1,114 1s. 2¼d., discharge £601 6s. 5¾d. Then occurs the first mention of something that has never yet succeeded and is still discussed to this day.

5th May 1731. Ordered that the Pharmacopoeia agreed upon do from this day take place! The physicians and surgeons were requested to confine their prescriptions to this, and the apprentices were to see that the patients took the medicines.

There was a new departure this day also in that the Treasurer was requested to purchase four £100 East India Bonds. This was done, the broker, Mr Benjamin Wright, offering his services free at any time if he could sometimes recommend a patient. This policy continued, and by June 1733 the infirmary owned seventeen of these Bonds.

On 13th October the Board were still fulminating about the cost of the medicines (they still are!), but 1732 begins with yet another new proposal, at ·first turned down, but later accepted, that of a resident (or journeyman) apothecary. On 29th March Sir Brownlow Sherrard presented the infirmary with the iron chest, which is thus the only relic the present hospital possesses of the second infirmary. This was for its monies and papers; the keys were held by Mr Hayward, Captain Hudson, and Mr Le Grand. In April 1732 the accounts were even more satisfactory, the charges being £1,280 18s. 8d. and the discharges only £603 8s. 8d.

In June, the much disputed resident apothecary was appointed (after a short list had been prepared following advertisements in the papers). He was Thomas Aldridge. The quest for a new house, or suitable ground to build on, was now in full swing and a Mr Fido paid for advertisements in the *Daily Advertiser* for this purpose. So begins the fateful year 1733. One John Thomas is elected messenger and the silver badge is taken from the iron chest for him to wear, and a Dr Coates appears on the scene. He was to play a big part in the infirmary's affairs later. On 13th June the good-hearted Mr William Green, who had been elected Vice-President to the Bishop of Winchester, as President of the Board of Trustees offered certain houses in Castle Lane and Petty France to the infirmary for their use. A committee consisting of Drs Tessier, Stuart, Wasey, and Mr Aspinwall, Captain Hudson, Mr Eyres, Mr Moody, Mr Steadman, Mr· Churchill and Sergeant-Surgeon Amyand were appointed to inspect them and report on their suitability. The succeeding events brought to a head the dissensions of the two sections of opinion in the Trustees and resulted in the formation of St George's Hospital!

5
The Birth of St George's Hospital

'A letter being also read from Mr Lane to Dr Stuart relating to his house at High Park corner and a question being put whether the said House would be convenient for ye use of this Infirmary. It was passed in the Negative.'

Westminster Hospital Minutes, Vol. 3, p. 343,
7th September 1733

The stormy events of the next four months appear at this length of time almost incredible. Despite all that was written about it at the time, the motives that led a minority of the Trustees and almost all the staff to split themselves off from the majority are, on the face of it, arbitrary in the extreme. The committee set up on 13th June reported on 20th June that Mr Green's houses were very conveniently sited on freehold land and very suitable for the purposes of an infirmary. It was arranged that a treaty should be prepared with Mr Green, and notice was sent to Mr John Nicholls that the Society hoped to vacate the Chapel Street premises. It was later alleged that the Chapel Street house was old and ruinous, but this is not borne out by a survey carried out by Mr Steadman and Mr Dagsby

on 28th March 1733, who reported that the foundations were sound and only a few minor repairs were needed.

A Special General Board was held on 7th September 1733. There was a very large attendance. It was put to the meeting that Mr Green's houses be taken, and this was agreed. A letter from Mr Lane to Dr Stuart offering the use of Lanesborough House at Hyde Park corner was then read. It was decided that this house was not suitable (see facsimile of the minutes). A further committee consisting of those of 13th June and Dr Ross, Mr Cheselden, Sergeant-Surgeon Dickens, with Dr John Wiggan as Chairman, was appointed to draw up a final contract with Mr Green for the renting of one or more of his three houses.

33

This committee reported back to the General Board of 27th September 1733, and a draft lease was produced and read. There followed considerable debate and (it seems) no little heat. Finally, it was decided that the committee should not proceed further in the matter for six weeks. During this time, it transpired later, Dr Stuart had actually signed a lease (on 20th September) of Lanesborough House for seven years! His co-lessees were Drs Stewart and Tessier, Sergeant-Surgeons Dickens and Amyand and a Mr Thomas Smith. At a Board meeting of 9th October Mr Green (who refused to take the chair because of his own involvement in the matter) laid a Paper before the meeting explaining how he had, with much difficulty, tried to discuss the matter with the Bishop of Winchester and had not succeeded. None the less, the Trustees, on hearing that the Hyde Park house had been taken by Dr Stuart and his friends, took the following action—

1. The Charter was not to be proceeded with at this time.
2. The Petition to the King was also suspended.
3. The Books of the infirmary were to be delivered to Mr Pengrey Hayward.

Finally, a definite contract was agreed on with Mr Green. On the next day Dr Stuart, Dr Wasey and Mr Wilkie resigned from the infirmary staff. The Board requested the Sergeant-Surgeons to attend the infirmary when requested on any extra-ordinary occasion, to which they were pleased to consent, but although nothing so definite as a resignation is

Westminster Hospital Minutes for 7th September 1733.

recorded, their services to the infirmary ceased at this time, as did that of Dr Tessier. There remained Mr Cheselden, but he did not resign his post. He took the more profitable course—he joined the St George's staff also! The Reverend Mr Trebeck had tried his hand at pouring oil on troubled waters by suggesting that subscribers to the new institution should continue to be subscribers to the old. It is pleasing to note that many, including Dr Stuart, did in fact do this. None the less, the secession was concluded.

The Birth of St George's Hospital

Many reasons were put forward but one, at least, is plausible. There had been over the last year an accession of more wealthy Trustees who found it much easier to go to Hyde Park Corner in the fields, as it then was, than to dive into the teeming and, no doubt, odoriferous back streets of lower Westminster. It should be noted that the Bishop of Winchester was one of these, and he attended the first meeting at Lanesborough House. Soon his opinion was being asked 'touching the division of the cash in the bank there' (i.e. at Chapel Street).

Captain Hudson, now a St George's man, was desired not to part with his key to the iron chest without the order of their Board, and letters were exchanged as follows—

> Hyde Park Corner,
> 23rd November 1733.
>
> Sir,
>
> Our general board, to show the desire of a coalition with yours in Chapel Street, have unanimously resolved that they would at any time be ready to concert proper measures with yours to render the common charity more extensive and effectual. This they have desired me to communicate to you that, if any expedient could be found to bring about such a coalition, nothing would be wanting on their part towards completing it. I am also to acquaint you that such of your subscribers as are subscribers here are very desirous that the treasure locked up in the chest should be laid out for the purpose to which it was intended. And if any difficulty should arise in the distribution of it, in which they claim a right, they are willing to refer it to the private determination of the Lord Chancellor, Master of the Rolls or Lord Chief Baron, or to two or three indifferent persons of each board. In the meantime they have desired Captain Hudson not to part with his key without their consent. You will be pleased to lay this before your general board, that such measures may be taken by both boards as will best promote and extend the charity.
>
> Sir, your most obedient servant,
> (Signed) Jer. Griffith, Chairman

This letter was answered as follows in January—

> Public Infirmary in Westminster,
> 8th January 1733–4.
>
> Sir,
>
> Agreeably to your desire by your letter of 23rd of November last, Mr Hayward, our treasurer, laid the same before our quarterly general board, who are pleased to return for answer that conformable to your desires they will, as they have hitherto done, heartily use all expedients to render this charity as extensive and effectual as possible, and that they will duly apply the money in the chest to the purposes for which it was intended by the benefactors and donors, the distribution of which they are advised by council is lodged in them, as the majority of the society before your separation, according to the tenor of the subscription roll; and therefore conceive there can be no occasion for any reference about it.
>
> (Mark Thurston), Chairman

Dr John Wiggan, Physician to Westminster 1733–37. (National Portrait Gallery).

It was sufficient, and Captain Hudson yielded up his key a week later to the treasurer at Westminster. In accordance with the times both sides wrote and printed letters and pamphlets presenting their own case, no doubt, as Peachey says (in his *History of St George's Hospital*) with the idea of putting themeslves right with the wealthy public. From these emerge the picture of a small but active minority who were determined to have their own way, even if it was necessary to secede for this purpose.

When all had died down there was no doubt that whoever was right, the general public were the ones to gain by it, for there were now, in 1733, five hospitals, St Bartholomew's, St Thomas's, Westminster Infirmary, Guy's Hospital (founded in 1724) and St George's. This was a great improvement on the position of 1719.

During these dramatic events Westminster Infirmary had been putting its house in order. Immediately after the resignation of Stuart, Wasey and Wilkie, their places were filled by Charles Cotes (or Coates) and John Wigan (or Wiggan), physicians, and William Pyle, surgeon (16th October 1733). Cotes at this time was not qualified as a medical man at all! He had become a Doctor of Common Law (Oxon.) in 1732 and was a Fellow of All Souls. Indeed, it was not until 1736 that he became M.D. (Oxon.). The same year he married Cheselden's daughter, Wilhemina, and thereafter his progress was rapid. He became a candidate of the Royal College of Physicians in 1737 and a Fellow in 1738. Incidentally, he had become M.P. for Tamworth in 1734. He resigned in 1739, and in 1745 was instrumental in aiding Cheselden in intro-

36

The Birth of St George's Hospital

ducing the bill into Parliament which separated the surgeons from the barbers. John Wigan was educated at Westminster School and Christ Church, Oxford, when he graduated in 1723. He was well known as a translator and editor of medical works. In 1737 he went to Jamaica as physician and secretary to his old friend Edward Trelawny, and having married there, died soon after.

William Pyle of Cecil Street had been a subscriber since March 1732. He was a member of the Barber-Surgeons Company and was an examiner for the surgeons in 1745 when the Act was passed separating the surgeons from the barbers. He deserves a note, for he seems to have been the first Westminster surgeon to have brought his pupils to the infirmary, for which he was duly reprimanded (*see* Chapter 9). With John Price, who was appointed Assistant Surgeon in 1733, these gentlemen constituted the new staff. It was necessary, however, to elect a new apothecary also, for Mr Aldridge had gone to Hyde Park corner, and on 16th October 1733, Mr Wm Taylor took up this post. Fortunately, at this time one person remained at her post, the Matron, Mrs Alden. There can be no doubt that the events of this stormy year must have put a great strain on the loyalties of those who had become subscribers to the Society and it is a great tribute to them that so many remained steadfast to the ideals which had promoted the original foundation. Without them the Society might well have perished and this institution would never have succeeded in reconstituting itself to become what it is today.

Fortunately, the infirmary did not lack friends,

William Pyle, Surgeon to Westminster 1735–48, by Robert Edge Pine, presented by Mr Henry Watson in 1767.

some of whom were powerful and influential. On 28th November 1733 Sir Hans Sloane, Bart. and Dr Richard Mead (Cheselden's friend), both became subscribers and offered their 'advice and assistance on any extraordinary occasion'. Indeed, Dr Richard Mead remained in that capacity until 1757 but there is no written record of his services to the infirmary. The fascinating feature of the minutes at this time is the cool and eminently practical manner in which business was transacted. On 8th January 1733/34, the Trustees signed a 21-year lease of Mr Green's houses in Castle Lane with Drs Wigan and Cotes as tenants and lessees. The rent of the three houses was to be £60 a year. In March more 'Rules' were made. The patients were to eat their midday meal between 12 noon and 2 p.m., they were to be in bed by 10 p.m. Lady Day to Michaelmas, and by 9 p.m. from Michaelmas to Lady Day. The amount of meat for patients was cut to 8 oz and stringent rules were made concerning the offering and the taking of gratuities. However, a concession was made—the night nurses were allowed one pint of ale for breakfast. In March also, Mr Taylor, the apothecary, resigned and Mr Charles Harris was appointed in his stead. On 8th April an event occurred which must have greatly heartened the Trustees—Queen Caroline sent £100 for the infirmary, and despite everything, the yearly audit was amazingly good. Charge £3,032 9s. 6¾d. to a discharge of £707 19s. 9¼d. But, alas, the faithful Mrs Alden resigned for reasons of ill health: she was given the thanks of the Board and a gratuity of £2 2s., and Mrs Elizabeth Owen

was elected Matron in her stead on 22nd May 1734. During the year additional buildings were erected at the new houses and all was got ready for the move. Indeed, they had to pay Mr Titchcroft, surveyor, £250 for the workmen. Rather than let the infirmary sell its cherished East India Bonds at a discount Mr Green lent them the money out of his own pocket. There remains to be mentioned two patients, Jane Radford, 'accidentally hurt by a coach'—the first traffic accident; and Thomas James who was the first patient in the new infirmary—cut for the stone. Just before the end of the year an event took place which seems to have made up the Trustees' minds about doing something for incurable patients. They received a gift of £400 for this purpose from an unknown person. At this, and future meetings, it was decided to form a fund, the Incurables Fund, and to admit as many incurable patients of both sexes as the interest on the fund would support. Another proposal at this time strikes a little harshly on modern eyes—uniform for the patients. Finally (Christmas Day 1734), Sir Joseph Jekyll, Master of the Rolls, became President in place of the Bishop of Winchester, just deceased.

The patients were transferred and Westminster Infirmary took up its new quarters in Castle Lane on 24th February 1735. They were to remain there for almost 100 years.

It is instructive to note the fates that befell the seceding members of the staff. Dr Stuart remained attached to St George's until 1736 when he resigned. He died in 1742, a poor man, as rumour has it, due to unwise speculation.

The Birth of St George's Hospital

A totally different fate befell Dr Wasey. He became President of the Royal College of Physicians from 1750 to 1753, and when he died in 1757 left to the Royal College his case book, which on examination shows cases of Dr Stuart also, from Westminster! A curious ending to such a happy beginning.

Sergeant-Surgeon Amyand died in 1740, following a disastrous fall from his horse in Greenwich Park. Sergeant-Surgeon Dickens died in 1747 it is believed, but he does not seem to have made much noise in the scientific world. The Bishop of Winchester became the first President of St George's, yet he died shortly afterwards. Dr Tessier died in 1742. Mr Cheselden's later career is described in the next chapter. We should be grateful to these men for the 'good they did lived after them, the evil was interred with their bones'.

Extracts from the case-book of Drs Stuart and Wasey, 1723–24. (Royal College of Physicians)

6

From Infirmary to Hospital, 1735–1793

'. . . that Benj. Lewis be admitted Incurable.'
Westminster Hospital Minutes, Vol. 4, p. 14,
26th March 1735

The Trustees, on their move to Mr Green's three houses at the junction of Castle Lane, James Street, Petty France and Horseferry Road (*see* map) were, above all else, interested in the two new proposals mentioned at the end of Chapter 5. These were to 'cloathe' the patients in a uniform manner and to establish the arrangements for the incurable patients. In the 'Proceedings of the Trustees' for 1735 these two projects are set out as follows—

'The Society have lately enlarged their Charity in two Particulars, viz. Cloathing the Poor whilst they continue in the House and entertaining Patients deemed Incurable; to which they have been encouraged by Benefactions given for both these Purposes.'
'The Patients upon their Admittance are cloathed

in decent, warm and distinguishing Apparel, which they leave behind them when discharged: And it is hoped That this Regulation will produce the desired Effects of Cleanliness, Health and good Order.'

The Board had not moved from Chapel Street without taking some thought for the problems ahead of them. They had spent, for the times, the quite considerable sum of £809 17s. on converting the houses for their new use. Even so, a new 'window or windows' had to be put into the men's ward in July. If the site is examined on Roque's Map of 1746 it is seen that the area was very open by comparison with Chapel Street. To the north, across Petty France, a row of houses and gardens separated them from St James's Park. To the south were orchards and fields stretching down to the

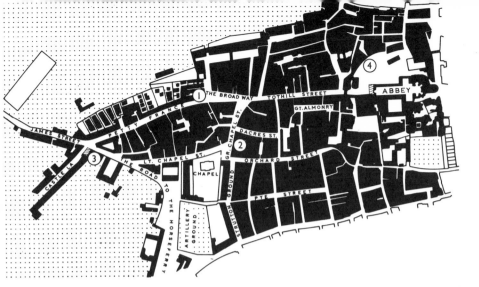

Maps to show the location of the Hospital in:
1. *1720*
2. *1724*
3. *1735*
4. *1834*
Below: in modern times.

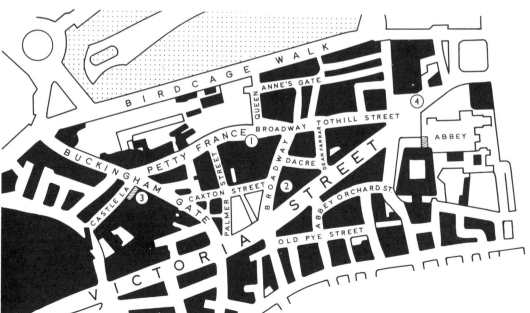

Thames. To the south-east Horseferry Road led past their neighbours, Lady Dacre's Almshouses (Emanuel Hospital) and the 'Blew Coat School', founded in 1709 by Mr William Green Snr. The road then passed Palmer's Almshouses and the west side of the Artillery ground to turn east by the end of leafy Rochester Row to pass the Grey Coat School. To the north-west, James Street led past Rosamund's Pond to Buckingham House. To the west were open fields beyond the row of houses on the other side of Castle Lane, while Castle Lane itself led to the Stag Brewery, which belonged to Mr William Green.

From the start the idea of the Establishment for Incurables touched the public conscience in a remarkable way. The Board received many gifts and legacies for this fund and for a considerable period it exceeded the General Purpose Funds. The largest donation was that of Mr Andrew Highstreet in 1805, a donation of £5,339, his name being given to the ward for male incurables, until the late 1920s. Indeed, in 1948 there were still four incurable patients, the last of whom, Miss Bessie Southern, died in 1962 at the age of 89, having been on the establishment since 1933. To gain admittance to the establishment, the patients, having been deemed incurable by the physicians and surgeons and having no means of support, were proposed to the Board after an interval of 21 days. The Board then admitted them on the understanding that, if they recovered or if other means for their maintenance were found, they would be discharged. Otherwise, they were looked after for the rest of their lives.

There exists a minute book containing records of their cases, one entry of which is illuminating—it refers to a patient 'admitted by mistake some two and a half years past'! The Board decided to open 31 beds at first but this rose to 37 quite rapidly: in 1742 there were 86, in 1753—83, and in 1757—98. On 2nd July 1735 a novel type of patient was admitted—a man named John Hayes, at the request of Mr Cheselden, to have his cataract 'couched' by him. This, the first eye operation specifically mentioned, was successful. Mr Cheselden had been elected Surgeon to Queen Caroline in 1727, but in 1731 an unfortunate scandal arose, which caused him to lose favour at Court. It was known that the Queen was deaf, and that it worried her considerably. Mr Cheselden suggested that he should perform an operation on the ear of a convicted felon (presumably a deaf one) with a view, one presumes, of attempting it on the Queen later, if he was successful. However, someone talked too much, and it got into all the papers (and the Walpole letters) in many garbled forms. The operation was never performed, and Mr Cheselden lost his appointment at Court and the favour of the Queen.

He resigned his hospital posts in 1739, at the early age of 51, to become Resident Surgeon at the Royal Chelsea Hospital. He died at Bath, in 1752, and his tomb may be seen at the Royal Chelsea Hospital. On his retirement the following resolution was passed by the Board—

'That the thanks of the Society be given to Wm Cheselden, Esq. for the long and voluntary assistance given to the patients of this Infirmary by many

From Infirmary to Hospital, 1735–1793

PHYSICIANS		SURGEONS	
John Wigan, MD (Oxon)	1733–1737	*Consulting Lithotomist and Ophthalmic Surgeon*	
Charles Cotes, DCL, MD (Oxon)	1733–1739	William Cheselden, FRS	1733–1739
Benjamin Hoadley, FRS, MD (Cantab)	1736–1746		
Thomas Wilbraham, FRS, DCL,		*Surgeons*	
MD (Oxon)	1739–1761	William Pyle	1733–1748
James Hawley, MD (Oxon)	1739–1750	John Price (Asst Surgeon 1733–1735)	1735–1746
John Barker, MD (Oxon)	1746–1748	John Pyle (Asst Surgeon 1735–1746)	1746–1788
Gowin Knight, MD	1748–1752	Robert Heathfield (Asst Surgeon	
William Coxe, MD (Cantab)	1750–1757	1746–1749)	1749–1755
Robert Watson, MD	1752–1754	William Baker	1749–1754
Sir Richard Jebb, FRS, MD (Aberdeen)	1754–1762	Thomas Gataker	1754–1760
Thomas Brooke, MD	1757–1766	James Wallace	1755–1762
Michael Morris, FRS, MD (Rheims)	1761–1791	Abraham Worley Humphreys	1760–1770
James Dargent, MD	1762–1788	Henry Watson, FRS	1762–1793
John Brickenden, MD	1766–1775	John Obadiah Justamond, FRS	1770–1786
George Hicks, MD	1775–1792	John Sheldon, FRS	1786–1788
George Paulet Morris, MD	1788–1810	William Lynn (Asst Surgeon 1787–1788)	1788–1834
William Blackburne, MD	1791–1794	William Richard Morel	1788–1823

and successful operations as Lithotomist, and by readily contributing his experience and advice on all occasions as Consulting Surgeon, to the great relief of the patients as well as credit and success of the Society in General.'

Cheselden's simple wooden operating table was preserved and placed, eventually, as one of the tables in the Students' Club in the Medical School built in 1885. It was, however, destroyed by a combination of ignorance and apathy in or about 1920.

Times were changing, and one of the signs of the times was the way medical and surgical staff were to be elected to the staff. Between 1733 and 1746 there were but two new members, Benjamin Hoadley, F.R.S. and Thomas Wilbraham, F.R.S. Hoadley was the son of the Bishop of Winchester who was so disliked by George II. He was born in 1706 in London and when

Augusta of Saxe-Gotha, Princess of Wales and mother of George III. The first Patron of Westminster Hospital. (National Portrait Gallery)

the time came for him to graduate at Cambridge he was refused a degree, but one year later, in 1728, he was created M.D. by royal decree! He moved in Court circles, becoming Physician to the King's Household in 1742, and in 1746 Physician to the Prince of Wales's Household. It was noted that he 'possessed the common sense to use his worldly advantages to his best ends'. He was a great friend of Hogarth and of Garrick, and even wrote plays which were performed publicly. Their merit may be judged by the comment made on the best one: 'After Ranger (the hero) the next best character is Ranger's hat.' Yet he was a humane man, lively and well informed. It is no doubt due to his influence that Augusta of Saxe-Gotha, the Dowager Princess of Wales and mother of George III, became the first Patroness of the Infirmary in 1738. Thomas Wilbraham, F.R.S., D.C.L., M.D.(Oxon), who was a different sort of man altogether from Benjamin Hoadley, rose to the post of Treasurer of the Royal College of Physicians.

In 1746, John Price, the Surgeon of the Infirmary, died, and for the first time an election was held to fill a vacancy. In this election all subscribers were allowed to vote. In the event, it was necessary not only to fill the vacancy of Surgeon but also to elect a new Assistant Surgeon. John Pyle, son of William Pyle, was elected unanimously as Surgeon, and Robert Heathfield was elected Assistant Surgeon with 183 votes to William Baker's 111 votes and Arthur Wind's 45 votes. From then onwards this method of election prevailed until quite recent times. John Pyle, like his father, William, served the infirmary and hospital

From Infirmary to Hospital, 1735–1793

until his death. He became Master of the Corporation of Surgeons in 1772–73, but neither he nor his father have left any trace in the literature of the day.

The building did not, of course, remain static in size. From time to time additions and improvements are noted; eventually two other houses were acquired and the freeholds of all the sites were eventually obtained. The plumbing, of course, being by cesspools, which had to be pumped out into the drain running past the building, created much trouble. So too, did a neighbour, Mr Prince, who kept pigs; it required legal action for him to abate this nuisance.

A new phenomenon had ushered in the reign of George III in 1760. This was a municipal conscience. J. H. Plumb writes—

'Westminster . . . pioneered the way. A body of enterprising citizens between 1761 and 1765 secured Private Acts of Parliament by which they were enabled to levy a house rate in return for providing paving and lighting. They had the right to sue if any local anarchist refused to pay . . . the improvement in the social amenities of Westminster was startling.'

Still another phenomenon occurred that tended to upset Westminster's traditional isolation; in 1758, Westminster Bridge was opened. Even before then, accidents of all kinds had been so numerous that four beds had been set aside for them in 1753, and the 'Proceedings' of that year strikes a modern note when it refers to the small room to the right of the front door where severe accident cases were to be admitted and

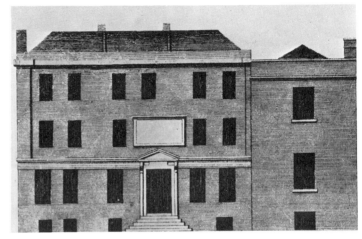

The Third Hospital, James Street, 1735–1834.

where they could be attended to (a version of an intensive care unit). It also foreshadowed isolation wards by stating that the above room could be used for nursing patients whose condition was so 'noisesome' as to render them distressing to the other patients.

Dirt was, of course, a great problem, but measures taken to alleviate this evil sometimes brought unexpected results in their train. In 1758, the then Matron, Mrs Gregory, engaged a charwoman to scrub the house at night. This apparition so grossly insulted, abused and frightened a male patient that he fell into fits, in which he died. The Board reprimanded the Matron for washing the wards at an unreasonable hour!

45

Despite the care taken, the inevitable concomitant of dirty people and wooden beds occurred. The place became, *horresco referrens*, infested with bed bugs, *Cimex lectularius*, and the great expert of the day, Mr Thomas Tiffen, was called in. He stated he would cleanse all the apartments and beds within three weeks for £20. This was in March 1764. He was still at work in 1769, being now paid one shilling a bed.

The wards were long and narrow and must have been uncomfortable in cold weather, for the fireplace was at the far end, leaving the area near the door unheated. There were no lamps, except in the passages and over the front door. All other illumination was by candlelight and the Board made a great fuss over economy in this respect, even restricting the House Surgeon to two candles a night (1792).

But despite these and other domestic annoyances, progress was being made, for on 7th November 1767, proposals were put forward to build an operating room at a cost of £100. This room was renovated and the north window was blocked up and another opened on the south side in July 1768. About this time, too, it was decided to change the title from infirmary to hospital, and on 4th August 1770, the following sign was put up—

'The Westminster Hospital for Sick and Lame Patients instituted in 1719—Establishment for Incurables begun in 1734. The whole supported by Subscriptions and Benefactions.'

The wars of the later part of the eighteenth century tended to reduce receipts and many strange ways of making money appear. Thus, the fortunate fact of the popular appeal of Handel's music coincided with the centenary of his birth, and many performances of his works brought money to the hospital. 'Messiah' at St Margaret's, in 1779, fetched in £250, 'Judas Maccabeus', in 1781, £151. From concerts in the Abbey the hospital received one-third of the proceeds: in 1784—£1,000, in 1785—£1,800, in 1786—£1,300 and in 1787—£1,400. Later, as Spencer drily says, musical festivals tended to become failures so far as the hospital was concerned.

The onward march of the hospital became punctuated, as it were, by a series of most remarkable members of the staff.

Sir Richard Jebb, 1754–62, was Physician Extraordinary to George III and Physician in Ordinary to the Prince of Wales. He was much beloved by his colleagues and his patients—'I will have Jebb,' said George III, yet he was so eccentric as to be almost certifiable. He is buried in the Abbey. Then, in 1762, Henry Watson, F.R.S., anatomist and surgeon, joined the staff. He had been on the staff of the Middlesex Hospital from 1751 to 1762, and was the first Professor of Anatomy at the Corporation of Surgeons, where he became Master on two occasions, 1785–86 and 1788–89. He was accomplished, learned, kind and a good teacher to those he knew. To the end of his days, however, he persisted in wearing the clothes of a bygone era, a curled wig, a full-cuffed coat with a number of huge buttons, a cocked hat and a cane. He died at the age of 91 (still on the staff).

He had as a colleague for many years John Obadiah

46

From Infirmary to Hospital, 1735–1793

Justamond, F.R.S., Surgeon to Her Majesty's Regiment, the Queen's 2nd Dragoon Guards, a man who spent more time with the regiment or on the Continent evading his debtors (says Langdon-Davies) than ever he spent at the hospital. Yet he was the first member of the staff to treat cancer with chemicals, using a paste of arsenic and hemlock to treat what are called rodent ulcers. The Medical School library has a copy of his Surgical Lectures addressed to Mr Henry Watson, F.R.S., Senior Surgeon to The Westminster Hospital and to the rest of the Medical Faculty of that excellent Institution.

Then, finally, John Sheldon must be noted. He was born in London in 1752 and became an apprentice of Henry Watson: while he was still a student he taught Anatomy at Watson's private museum in Tottenham Court Road until it was, for one reason or another, wrecked by an infuriated mob! He then opened his own school and published a book called *History of the Absorbent System*. He also published an account of the post-mortem findings on Matthew Maty, the principal Librarian at the British Museum. All these things made him well known. What made him notorious was his ascent in a balloon at 12 noon on 16th October 1784. He is thus the first member of the staff to travel by air. He claimed to be the first Englishman to have been up in a balloon. The facts are briefly as follows.

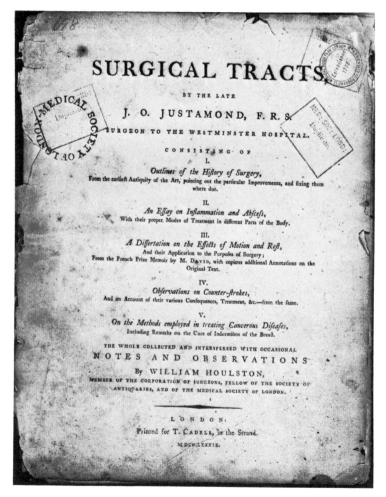

Title page of Mr Justamond's 'Surgical Tracts'. (Medical School Library)

Mr J. V. Shelden, F.R.S., Surgeon to Westminster, 1786–88; the first medical aviator. (Royal College of Surgeons)

The first balloon ascent was in France by Pilâtre de Rozier and the Marquis d'Arlandes on 21st November 1783. On 24th August 1784 a man called Tytler, in Edinburgh, made a brief hop of 300 feet straight up and down again. The first flight in England was by Lunardi, an Italian, from the Honourable Artillery Company's ground at Finsbury on 15th September 1784. On 4th October 1784, Sadler is alleged to have made an ascent of three-quarters of an hour. The event is fully described by Jackson's *Oxford Journal* but no eye-witness of this event was ever found! There were plenty of witnesses for Sheldon's flight with Jean-Pierre Blanchard on 16th October. They left from Lochées Military Academy, Little Chelsea, to the 'huzzas' of the mob, and got as far as Sunbury, where the balloon came down. Sheldon got out and the crafty Blanchard hurriedly took off again, travelling as far as Rumsey, hotly pursued by Sheldon on horseback! An apt comment of the day was the following 'Tombstone Epithet'—

> 'Adventuring in an Air Balloon
> To raise a Great Renown
> Science and Art did grieve to Think
> How much he let it down.'

The Art refers to the fact that he was Professor of Anatomy at the Royal Academy from 1783 to 1808. Sheldon was only on the staff from 1786 to 1788, when his health failed and he retired to Exeter. Here he recovered, joined the staff of the infirmary there, and produced yet another singularity. This was a poisoned harpoon to kill whales. Although a sick man, he even

48

William Lynn, Surgeon to Westminster 1788–1834, P.R.C.S. 1825.
(Royal College of Surgeons)

went to Greenland to test it out. His crowning singularity, however, was to keep the embalmed body of a beautiful young woman patient (under glass) in his bedroom. The poor cadaver, after his death, passed to the Royal College of Surgeons, and survived, a ghastly travesty of the human form until it was destroyed in a German air raid in 1941. Mr Shelden died peacefully in his cottage by the River Exe in 1808.

During these years there was one man who quietly, perhaps too quietly, was engaged in performing his own and other people's work as well. This was William Lynn. He began his career at the hospital in 1775 as the apothecary's pupil and was a friend and pupil of John Hunter. He became Assistant Surgeon in 1787 and Surgeon in 1788, and retired at the age of 81 in 1834! Clarke says of him, 'Lynn was one of the most skilful of surgical artists. Nothing could be more admirable than his use of the knife when he made up his mind, which he did carefully before he proceeded to operate.' In 1792 his colleague, Morel, had, against his advice, attempted to remove a diseased parotid gland from a woman. The operation was followed later by a secondary haemorrhage. Lynn exposed the common carotid artery in the neck and applied a single ligature. The haemorrhage ceased, the patient suffered no ill-effects, but died a fortnight later from debility. It was probably the first time the carotid had been ligatured in a human patient. Such was the quality of this quiet man who was to have such a reputation as a teacher and surgeon in the years to come.

7
Power, Policy and Presidents, 1793–1834

In October 1793, Mr Henry Watson died, 'having imprudently gone into the street without his nightcap, upon a false alarm of fire, he being then very frail from an attack of the palsy'. He was 91. It was the end of an era. He was succeeded by Anthony Carlisle, his newly qualified late resident pupil, aged 25. Anthony Carlisle was born at Stillington, County Durham, on 15th February 1768. He came to London at the age of 17 and immediately his great talent, that of making

Sir Anthony Carlisle, F.R.S., Surgeon to Westminster 1793–1840, P.R.C.S., 1828, 1837.

friends, came to the fore. He studied Art under Sir Joshua Reynolds and Anatomy under John Hunter at the Great Windmill Street School. Here he won that irascible genius's approbation by 'making the first perfect cast of the labyrinth of the ear which he presented to Mr Hunter who was highly delighted with the acquisition'. His knowledge of, and interest in, comparative anatomy was so great that after John Hunter's death in 1793 he was offered the post of Curator to make the dissections and organise the Hunterian collection. He declined the offer but used his not inconsiderable influence to ensure that the Government purchased the collection, which was placed in the care of the College of Surgeons. His knowledge and interest in science also enabled him (in 1800) to perform a fundamental electrical experiment, the electrolysis of water. He received from Sir J. Banks, Bart., P.R.S., an account of Volta's electrical experiments and constructed a 'pile' (i.e. a battery) of 17 halfcrowns and 17 pieces of zinc separated by pieces of pasteboard soaked in salt water, 'the contacts being made sure by placing a drop of water on the upper plate Mr Carlisle observed a disengagement of gas round the touching wire' (W. Nicholson). In 1800 he became, also, F.R.S. Such then was the nature of the new Surgeon to the Hospital. As a surgeon he was adequate, introducing several simplicities such as thin straight-bladed amputation knives instead of the heavy curved blades previously used. He also introduced the carpenter's saw into surgery. Whether corresponding about flying machines with Sir George Cayley, hobnobbing with Royalty,

gossiping with Charles and Mary Lamb, 'for Carlisle is the best story teller I ever heard', said Charles Lamb, or offering to cure Coleridge of drug taking—there was an infectious gusto about the man which made everybody, especially his students, like and hero-worship him. He continued his connexion with the world of art by following John Sheldon as Professor of Anatomy to the Royal Academy, a post he held from 1808 to 1824. He came at the right time, for it was an era of change, stimulated by the bitter war being waged against the French, a war, that with two short intermissions, was to last for twenty-two years, until Napoleon was finally defeated in 1815 at Waterloo.

Anthony Carlisle's surgical colleagues in 1793 were Mr Lynn, that quiet, skilled man, and William Richard Morel, who was so occupied by his Army duties as to be seldom able to perform his surgical duties at the hospital. Lieutenant Harry Smith of The Rifles, whose wife, the erstwhile Juanita Maria de los Dolores de Leon, later became *the* Lady Smith of Ladysmith, describes a professional encounter with Morrel—

'the ball was lodged on my ankle-joint, having partially divided the *tendo Achilles*.' [Two months later!] 'Soon after we reached Lisbon a Board was held consisting of the celebrated Staff Surgeon Morel who had attended me before, Higgins and Brownrigg. They examined my leg, I was all for the operation. Morel and Higgins recommended me to remain with a stiff leg of my own as better than a wooden one, for the wounds in Lisbon of late had sloughed so, they were dubious of the result.

Sir Alexander Crichton, Physician to Westminster 1794–1801.

Brownrigg said, "If it were my leg, out should come the ball." On which I roared out, "Hurrah, Brownrigg, you are the doctor for me." So Morel says, "Very well, if you are desirous we will do it *direclly*".

My pluck was somewhat cooled, but I cocked up my leg, and said, "There it is, slash away". It was five minutes, most painful indeed, before it was extracted. The ball was jagged, and the tendonous fibres had so grown into it, it was half dissected and half torn out, with most excruciating torture for a moment, the forceps breaking which had hold of the ball . . . . Thank God Almighty and a light heart, no sloughing occurred and before the wound was healed I was with the Regiment.'

The physicians at this time were George Paulet Morris, 1788–1810, Sir Alexander Crichton, M.D. (Leyden), who finally resigned to become physician to Tsar Alexander I of Russia, where he reorganised the State medical services and secured such control of epidemics that he received both British and Russian Orders of Knighthood. Writing many years later (in 1842) he gave a vivid picture of 'lower Westminster' at the time of his service as Physician to the Hospital: 'It had not then been well drained and as many parts of it were lower than the river at high water, it partook at times of the unhealthy malaria of marsh land so that malaria and bad intermittents (fevers) prevailed among the poor.'

Charles Dickens knew this area well; in *David Copperfield* he writes—

'The neighbourhood was a dreary one at that time; as oppressive, sad and solitary as any about London . . . . Coarse grass and rank weeds straggled all over the marshy land in the vicinity. In one part,

Dr W. G. Maton, F.R.S., Physician to Westminster 1801–09.
(Royal College of Physicians)

carcasses of houses, inauspiciously began and never finished rotted away . . . . Slimy gaps and causeways winding among old wooden piles with sticky substances clinging to them like green hair, and the rags of last years hand bills offering rewards for drowned men fluttering above high water mark, led down through the ooze and slush to the ebb tide . . . it looked as if it had gradually decomposed in to that nightmare condition, out of the overflowing of the polluted stream.'

The other physician was Thomas Bradley, M.D. (Edin.), who was a schoolmaster until the age of 40! He did not succeed in practice, 'being retiring and uncertain in his opinion'. Yet he was a good teacher, two of his pupils becoming physicians to the hospital. The first, William George Maton, F.R.S., was an authority on botany and shells; he was also an antiquary. He had the good fortune of being at Weymouth at a time when the Royal Family was there. The Princess Amelia found a wild plant, *Arondo Epigajis* (a kind of reed) unfamiliar to her. Maton was recommended to Queen Charlotte as an expert botanist, he named the plant, and thus established a connexion with the Royal family, which later led to his becoming physician to the Duchess of Kent and her daughter, the Princess Victoria. He also attended her father the Duke of Kent as he lay dying of pneumonia at Sidmouth in the bitter cold and wet winter of 1819–20. It seems likely that Dr Maton was thus the link that ensured Queen Victoria's interest in the hospital throughout the rest of her life. Maton was Physician to the Hospital from 1800 to 1808. He was succeeded by Bradley's other pupil, Thomas Ayrton Paris, who was physician from 1809 to 1813, when he retired for some time to Weymouth on account of ill health. As a doctor he relied largely on the look of the patient, and wrote long and minutely compounded prescriptions. He later became President of the Royal College of Physicians from 1844 until he died in 1856.

Paris was renowned for his invention of the safety bar, a simple device which prevented premature explosion of the gunpowder then used in blasting. 'By this simple but admirable invention,' said a writer to *The Times*, 'Dr Paris saved more lives than many heroes have destroyed.'

Instructions issued to patients, c.1810.

*Dr Thomas Ayrton Paris, Physician to Westminster 1809–13,
P.R.C.P. 1844–56.* (Royal College of Physicians)

The hospital buildings to which these distinguished gentlemen were attached was nearing the end of its career. It consisted basically of five houses, the freeholds of which had been gradually acquired over the years. These were knocked together and rather ramshackle additions built on, so that ultimately it accommodated 100 patients (in the 1820s), but it suffered from trouble with its cesspools and blockage of the main drain in front of the hospital. These were perennial troubles. However, after the invasion scare of 1803 had died away, when the Trustees offered the hospital for the 'sole use of the Defenders of the Country in Case of Actual Invasion or Internal commotion', the hospital received several sizeable legacies.

54

Power, Policy and Presidents, 1793–1834

Thus, Andrew Highstreet of an old Westminster family (a Highstreet was a subscriber to the Grey Coats in 1703) left £5,339 to the Incurable Fund. In 1806, John Hollond, 'of Grafton Street and Paris', says Spencer, left £2,000. Later (in 1830), Edward Hollond, left £10,000. In 1808, Sir Francis Burdett gave £2,000, the first of many such sums. Furthermore, the hospital had the good fortune to acquire as President, Hugh Percy, third Duke of Northumberland who, with his brother Algernon Percy (who became the fourth Duke) were indefatigable in their efforts to promote the welfare of the hospital. These legacies and the obvious shortcomings of the old building produced a desire for change and improvement.

During this period there was trouble with the nursing arrangements due to the Board's endeavours to effect economy. The Matron, Mrs Mortteras, elected in 1794 after the death from illness of Mrs Turner, was put under considerable difficulties by this pinchparing policy. In 1791 there were eight nurses, four day and four night nurses, a cook, a housemaid and a washerwoman. In the period 1800–08 the number of nurses was cut down to six, four day and two night nurses. They were paid £8 8s. a year. (The cook was paid £10 10s. and the housemaid £7 7s. in the year.) In 1806 the Matron's salary was increased from £20 to £40 but she had to do the work of the steward as well. This saved the steward's salary but the Matron (not unnaturally) was soon found to be in difficulty through overwork. In 1803 there was much trouble in Mark Ward; one patient said that the nurse told him it didn't matter whether he took his medicine or not

Anthony White, Surgeon to Westminster 1823–49, P.R.C.S., 1834, 1841. Presented by himself.

as long as the physicians did not find out. Another patient complained of drunkenness, blasphemy and riot! The nurse was dismissed. Similar unsatisfactory findings were not uncommon during this period.

Yet the work of the hospital continued and the quality of the staff continued to improve. In 1806 Anthony White became Assistant Surgeon and, in

1823, on the retirement of Morel, full Surgeon. Anthony White was born in 1782 in Norton, County Durham and educated at Whitton-le-Wear. He went to Emmanuel College, Cambridge, at the age of 17 and graduated M.B. in 1804, when he came to London as Anthony Carlisle's apprentice. He was one of the most daring and brilliant surgeons the hospital has ever possessed, performing operations which, as they were done without anaesthetics, sound incredible. Thus, at Cambridge, he removed the upper jaw of a patient for chronic sepsis, with gratifying results. The sinuses healed, the protruding eyeball receded, and the lower jaw became mobile again. At Westminster he, against the advice of Lynn and Carlisle, who threatened to report him to the President of the College of Surgeons, excised the head of the femur for tuberculosis. The wound healed and the disease at that site was extirpated. Yet he had a severe fault—he was unpunctual. An hour late was nothing to him, a day late for a consultation not unknown. He is said to have been one week late on one occasion. However, as Clarke said from personal experience: 'But to go with him round the wards of the Westminster Hospital, when he did go round, was really a treat. He spoke little but it was always to the purpose, and what he said stamped him as a man of high philosophical, yet practical views of Surgery.' He suffered much in his later years from gout, which much restricted his movements. He had the good fortune, so says Charles Lamb, of having married such a lovely woman that when her portrait was exhibited at the Academy in 1809, the artist, Mr Daw, was elected a Royal Academician on the strength of it alone.

On the physicians' side in 1813, on the retirement of Bradley, Paris and Thomas Hume, 1809–13, there were elected Alexander Peter Buchan and George Leman Tuthill. Dr Buchan was M.D. (Leyden), and served until 1824. Tuthill was another friend of Charles and Mary Lamb. He was a physician to Bethlehem Hospital and treated Mary Lamb for her manic-depressive psychosis. In 1803, during the short-lived Peace of Amiens, he went to France and lingered too long, becoming a prisoner of the French on the resumption of the war. However, his diminutive vivacious French wife, of whom it was said that her hair was so long that it reached to her knees, got him released. She personally appealed to Napoleon on his return from hunting, and Tuthill was set free. In 1820, on the accession of George IV, both Anthony Carlisle and George Leman Tuthill were knighted at the instance of the Privy Council for professional merit.

However, the staff had not yet reached its peak, for it was not until 1823 that one of the most famous surgeons in England, Mr George James Guthrie, was elected to the staff, first as Assistant and later, in 1827, as Fourth Surgeon, a new post. In 1823 Mr Lynn was 70, Sir Anthony was 55, Mr White (now full Surgeon) was 41 and Mr Guthrie was 38.

Guthrie brought such a wind of change to the hospital that he practically disrupted the whole edifice, for he had two faults—he was tactless and somewhat of an opportunist. He was of Scots extraction, but born on 1st May 1785 at Wakefield. His father was a naval surgeon. At the age of 13 he was

George James Guthrie, F.R.S., Surgeon to Westminster 1827–43, P.R.C.S., 1833, 1842, 1854. (The Lancet, 1850)

invited by Mr Rush, the Inspector General of the Army Hospitals to become an army 'surgeon's mate', and in June 1800 went to the Army Hospital, York Hospital in Euston Square. But in March 1801,

Mr Keate, the Surgeon-General, refused to employ unqualified hospital mates any longer. Thus, Guthrie and his three other 'mates' were faced with a dilemma. The other three resigned, but Guthrie, at two days' notice, took the M.R.C.S. examination and passed. He was 16 years old. The College shortly afterward passed a regulation to prevent candidates acquiring the Diploma before the age of 21. He was immediately appointed Regimental Assistant Surgeon to the 29th Foot (now the Worcester Regiment). After service in North America he went to the Peninsula with Wellington in 1808 and was present at the battles of Roliça and Vimeiro (where he was wounded in both legs by a musket ball). On recovery, he was at Talavera, Albuera (where there were 3,000 wounded) and the sieges of Cuidad Rodrigo and Badajoz. After the Battle of Salamanca his masterly handling of the wounded won the approbation of Wellington, who later appointed him Deputy-Inspector of Hospitals, and he was finally present, in 1814, at the Battle of Toulouse, the last battle of the Peninsular War. At this time he made a collection of specimens of gunshot wounds of bone, collected no doubt from the victims of Sir Thomas Picton's rash attack, whose bodies, lying in their red tunics in the green water meadows, led them to be called the 'Flowers of Toulouse'. Two of these specimens can be seen to this day in the Medical School Museum. However, after the fighting ceased, 'Guthrie began to experience the usual gratitude of the British Government. The medical authorities at home refused to gazette his appointment as Deputy-Inspector on the score of youth'. He went on half-pay and by dint of much hard work acquired two private patients in 1815. He was pressed to go to Belgium but arrived there the day after the battle. Neither private patient spoke to him again. This then was the man, 'shrewd, quick, active and robust . . . voluble to a fault'. He said once, 'To become a successful eye surgeon a man must be prepared to ruin a whole hatfull of eyes.' His textbooks on surgery were famous, and his results of the treatment of battle casualties were unsurpassed for more than fifty years.

However, his reputation caused some jealousy among his colleagues and his tongue made enemies. He also had the misfortune to have as his pupil an even more hot-headed man, Hale Thomson. One day, in 1827, Guthrie was arguing hotly with Sir Charles Ferguson Forbes concerning the affairs of the Westminster Eye Hospital, which they had jointly founded, when suddenly, Hale Thomson interjected an insulting remark. Forbes immediately called him out and they fought a pistol duel on Clapham Common. Both missed, but the *Lancet,* then in the flower of its mocking youth, called him 'Bullet-proof Thomson' for many years to come. The affair reflected no credit on Guthrie.

The four surgeons, Lynn, Carlisle, White and Guthrie were all, in their time, President of the Royal College; Lynn in 1825, Carlisle in 1828 and 1837, White in 1834 and 1841 and Guthrie (who was made F.R.S. in 1827) in 1833, 1842 and 1854. Between 1829 and 1837, when the aged Mr Lynn died, they constituted four of the ten examiners of the College and, as the custom of the times did not allow students to be examined by their teachers, there was a rush of students to Westminster. Spencer quotes from the Surgeons' Pupil's Book the following sums paid in 1835: six Physicians' pupils paid £94 10s.— this was divided between the three physicians; the Surgeon's pupils paid £465, divided between the four surgeons. Particularly, people paid to be a pupil of Guthrie, who was greatly feared as an examiner, although he always claimed never to have failed a candidate by himself. It will be seen that Westminster had in those times a considerable reputation as a teaching centre. Once a year the *Lancet* published for the use of intending students a candid criticism of the London Teaching Hospitals. In 1833 it stated, on 28th September—

'The mode of clinical instruction (in Surgery) at this Hospital is what the Germans call "ambulatory" and is essentially conversational. Mr Lynn and Mr White are the most popular surgeons and continually impart lessons of the most genuine and practical wisdom, in a manner the most simple and unaffected. Sir Anthony Carlisle and Mr Guthrie are more oratorical in their communications and their instructions spontaneously assume the formal garb of lectures; Sir Anthony, however, is distinguished for the frequent enunciation of Pithy apothegms, some of which have truth to recommend them and all a certain degree of point and humour.'

One of the 'pithy apothegms' was: 'Medicine is an art founded in conjecture and improved by murder' (a remark which must have endeared him to his physician colleagues). It is not surprising that this continuing activity rendered the inadequacies of the James Street building more odious as the years passed and a powerful movement to rebuild became manifest. In 1819, the Centenary year, the Building Fund was inaugurated at a meeting at Willis's rooms (the old Almacks Club), with Anthony Carlisle as Secretary. Carlisle had, in 1818, says Spencer, written a sketch of the history of the Charity, but no trace of this has been found. Various sites were considered, even an amalgamation with Charing Cross Hospital.

The Broad Sanctuary site was cleared in 1824 but Church and State in the persons of the Abbey authorities and the Government of the day, were obstructive. There being no obvious progress, the Building Fund languished and the Hon. Phillip Pleydell-Bouverie made a shrewd report that there was not much hope of collecting the whole sum for years to come, but that if building started it was certain that people would come forward to aid in its completion. The Fund at the time amounted to £6,749 and there were not wanting many people who would patch up the James's Street building rather than branch out boldly into the financial dangers of an unknown future. Fortunately, his ideas prevailed and the Broad Sanctuary site (now, and for many years past, a car park) opposite the West door of the Abbey, was purchased for £6,000 from the Treasury in November 1831. Messrs Inwood's plans were adopted in February 1832, and the lead roofing was put on in December 1833. By 14th November 1834, patients were being transferred, and a Board meeting had already been held in the new building on 11th November. This new hospital, unique for Westminster in being built as a hospital, cost, including the site, £40,000. The old hospital, its site and its furniture (£736) were sold for £3,236. Despite the rebuilding, the invested funds of the hospital were £8,000 more in 1840 than in 1820, and a new hospital on a freehold site had been obtained. It is said that the two old pupils of the hospital, Mr Lynn and Sir Anthony Carlisle, personally collected £2,000 and £8,000 respectively for their hospital. As a note of interest, the co-treasurer with Pleydell-Bouverie from 1828 was a member of the Hoare family, Charles Hoare, a great-grand nephew of Mr Henry Hoare.

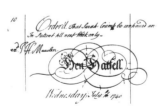

8

The Hospital in the Sanctuary

'Mr Rutherford Alcock is introduced by Sir Anthony
Carlisle to the Board as the House Surgeon.'
Westminster Hospital Minutes, Vol. 28, p. 321,
18th February 1829

This building was to last for more than 110 years
before it was finally pulled down in 1950. It served
its purpose as a hospital until the move to the St John's
Gardens site in 1939. During its 105 years of active life
it necessarily underwent many drastic alterations, yet
those of us who had the privilege of working in it are
proud to have done so. As a building it was old, out of
date perhaps, yet it still had an air of great dignity and
gave one most markedly, from its position, a sense of
being at the heart of the busy world itself. The original
building was described as Elizabethan with Henry VII
windows built of Suffolk brick with freestone facing.
It was originally only three storeys high with a deep
basement. There was a straight wide corridor running
the length of the building with two short projections at
the ends. The basic plan (*see* diagram) provided for
three wards leading off from these spurs. It was undoubtedly an advanced building for its day and the

wards were provided with what was regarded, then,
as a great innovation. This was a water-closet in each
ward, separated by a thin matchboarded partition
from the rest of the ward. Unfortunately, the Board
did not pay sufficient attention to the drainage, which

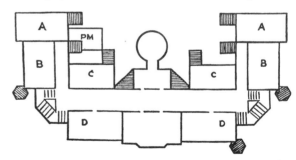

Ground plan of the Hospital in the Sanctuary. (from Langdon-
Davies).

60

Westminster Hospital 1834.

Westminster Hospital about 1840.

was by cesspool and a barrel drain, so that after a few years of use the minutes contain innumerable (and distressing) references to these early models of the sanitary engineer's art.

Immediately above the porch was the Board Room. This was a stately room with a fine aspect and, as recorded in the previous chapter, a meeting had been held there (11th November 1834) even before the building had been fully occupied. The meeting was held to elect an Assistant Surgeon, for William Bewicke Lynn became Fourth Surgeon on the final retirement of his father, William Lynn, at the age of 81.

The elder Lynn had been Surgeon since 1778, a period of 56 years, but though aged he was by no means senile. His last operation, carried out when he was past 80, was to remove a tumour the size of a large melon from a woman's breast. The reporter commented on the rapid, dexterous and intrepid manner in which the operation was performed. The wound healed speedily and the patient was in perfect health two months later. The old surgeon died in 1837 at the age of 84; it was said of him that he was the 'Nestor of the surgical profession, successful in a thousand capital operations but untutored in the use of the pen, he has carved his name with a Scalpel in the Temple of Fame.'

His son who followed him was a thoroughly capable surgeon but was by no means as able or distinguished as his father. The election of 11th November was a notoriously scandalous occasion because of the conduct of the successful candidate, the, by now, notorious Hale Thomson. Defeated by the younger Lynn

61

in the election of 1831 for the post of Assistant Surgeon, he redoubled his canvassing activities and became engaged to the Treasurer's daughter. At the election he was opposed by all the medical staff except Guthrie, but was elected by 169 votes to 100, the unsuccessful candidate being Maitland. It was said of Hale Thomson that he had come into a fortune, had not done the necessary work, and was a poor surgeon. Even Clarke, who befriended him later, said he possessed only one necessary attribute for a surgeon—that was bravery, and that he would have made an excellent surgeon to a cavalry regiment! Such an election was a poor omen for the success of the new building.

King William and Queen Adelaide became Patrons to the hospital on their accession in 1830, and in 1835 the Duchess of Kent (who paid 50 guineas) became a Vice-Patroness—this opened the way to the acceptance of the office of Patroness by Queen Victoria on her accession in 1837. Her great interest in the hospital continued through her reign and we are fortunate indeed that her descendants have continued this interest, so that Her Majesty, Queen Elizabeth II, is our present Patroness, a fact of which we are justly proud. In 1836 the hospital became incorporated by Act of Parliament, thus finally achieving what had been attempted in 1733. A further link with the Houses of Parliament came following the destruction of the old Houses of Parliament by fire in that year. For many years, until 1849 in fact, the records of the House of Lords were stored in one of the upper wards which the Governors felt they could not use for patients because of lack of funds. The new building

WESTMINSTER HOSPITAL STAFF 1834

Physicians		*Assistant Surgeon*	
Tristram Whittier	1823–1835	F. Hale Thomson	1834–1843
John Bright	1823–1843		
George Hamilton Roe, MD (Edin)	1825–1857	*The President*	
John Burne	1835–1843	His Grace the Duke of Northumberland,	
		KG	1813–1847
Surgeons		*Secretary to the Hospital*	
Sir Anthony Carlisle, FRS	1793–1840	Mr F. J. Wilson	1832–1878
Anthony White	1823–1849		
George James Guthrie, FRS	1827–1843	*The Matron*	
William Bewicke Lynn	1834–1852	Mrs F. Cox	1818–1847 (dec'd)

The Hospital in the Sanctuary

in 1834 could accommodate 106 in-patients, and about 1,000 in-patients were admitted annually, with 15,000 out-patient attendances; but within twenty years the pressure on the available space had become very great indeed. This was partly due to the increase in the number of patients presenting for treatment, and partly due to the necessity of accommodating the Medical School at the back of the hospital (*see* Chapter 9) in 1852.

It was unfortunately true, at this most critical time when the hospital staff and the Governors should have been united in their endeavours to direct the affairs of the new hospital, that there were sharp divisions among them. It was also unfortunate for them too, that the *Lancet* was keenly looking for any evidence of abuse of power or inefficiency in the hospitals of the day. It is amazing to our present-day ideas that there were persons working in the hospitals only too eager to supply ammunition, real or false, for this campaign. In 1838 the blow fell on the ageing Sir Anthony Carlisle. In 1820 he had delivered the Hunterian Oration, delivered annually in honour of the great John Hunter. It will be recalled that Sir Anthony had been Hunter's pupil, one who had inherited his love of, and great interest in, comparative anatomy. He chose for his subject 'The Anatomy of the Oyster' because he was keenly interested in the relationship between the various forms of integuments possessed by differing creatures: skin, hair, hide and the shells of various molluscs and the way these structures, which in their outer layers do not possess blood vessels, are formed. The editor of the *Lancet,* Thomas Walkley,

either did not understand the reason behind this choice of subject or chose to be offended by it. At any rate, he presumed to be insulted by what he did not understand and Sir Anthony Carlisle became 'Sir Anthony Oyster'. He attacked him on the subject of a man called Thomas Holmes, admitted to the hospital with an injured arm, who subsequently developed delirium tremens. Sir Anthony had not seen him on admission, but passing through the wards some days later he noticed that Holmes was in delirium and was causing discomfort to the other patients. Thereupon he signed a certificate of insanity which he left with the House Surgeon so that if necessary, and if the patient needed it, the certificate could be signed by a second medical man and the patient could then be removed as insane.

The attack by the *Lancet* caused the Board to take action and a committee was formed to go into the matter. This committee, which met on 19th October 1838, consisted of about fourteen medical staff and seven lay members of the Board of Governors. It came out at the inquiry that the patient was a heavy drinker, that he had had previous attacks, and that the certificate had been supplied by Sir Anthony at the request of the Chairman of the committee, Mr Bicknall who, visiting the hospital at a time when the patient was furiously violent, had ordered him to be put into a straitjacket. Further evidence showed where the *Lancet* had got its story. It was from the Apothecary, Mr D. O. Edwards and the House Surgeon, Bury Dasent. Mr D. O. Edwards rather ingenuously added, 'Our only object in publishing the case was to preserve an instance of the efficiency of large doses of opium in the treatment of delirium tremens'. He then went on to state that the Board had to consider Sir Anthony's fitness for his hospital duties in the light of the case. After other violent attacks and counter-attacks, including a peculiarly spiteful attack by, of all people, Hale Thomson, it was unanimously agreed, 'That the charges against Sir Anthony Carlisle are not proven, and that this Board adjourn *sine die*.' One year later the *Lancet* published an account of a surgical round by Sir Anthony, written by Clarke, who rather ridiculed the old gentleman. Sir Anthony, who had not thought that Clarke was attending the round for this purpose, was somewhat annoyed. He told the students that if they ever saw Clarke in the hospital he would be obliged if they would 'rough handle him a little'. Clarke was told of this, paid his fee and became a Governor. When he attended the next weekly Board he was recognised and had to jab his umbrella into the eye of one student so as to escape into the sanctuary of the Board Room. The Treasurer, acting as Chairman, was furious. He called up the ring-leaders of the students and threatened to dismiss them if they persisted in their attack on Clarke. The ring-leaders apologised, but when Clarke left the hospital they pursued him with so much fury that he was forced to take refuge in a local public house. Sir Anthony no doubt felt that he had had the better of *that* encounter.

Sir Anthony died on 2nd November 1840—it is one of the saddest things that this great son of Westminster should be remembered by his conduct in the last years of his life. As a young man he was brilliant; he even coined a new word in the English language, for Mr C. E. Drew found that the word 'hibernate' was first used by Sir Anthony in his Croonian lecture of 1804. He was buried very quietly in Kensal Green Cemetery, and his old apprentice Anthony White, caused the Board of Governors to pass a special minute stating the many ways in which the hospital was obliged to their late Senior Surgeon.

But the scandals continued, centred mainly round Hale Thomson, who had succeeded in forming a very large band of supporters, including one of the Canons of Westminster and the Vicar of St Margaret's. The other smaller party consisted of the rest of the medical staff and two popular nonconformist preachers. In 1843, George James Guthrie, F.R.S., retired from active surgical work and became Consulting Surgeon to the infirmary. This enabled Hale Thomson to become Surgeon and Guthrie's son to become Assistant Surgeon; this was Guthrie's second son, Charles G. Guthrie. He was an excellent surgeon but he fell ill and had to resign his post at the end of the year, being re-elected in 1850. In 1845 things came to a head, Board meetings were so stormy that Clarke suggested that the hospital must have been built over the old Westminster Cockpit! Finally a charge was laid before the House Committee accusing Hale Thomson of incompetence. A sort of trial was held. Clarke collaborated in Hale Thomson's defence (a curious position in which to find an assistant editor of the *Lancet*) on Mr D. O. Edwards's suggestion, and the charges were refuted easily.

Hale Thomson continued on the staff until 1850

64

The Hospital in the Sanctuary

when he became Consulting Surgeon. He died in 1860, alone in his rooms in Clarges Street, with an empty bottle of chlorodyne beside him, a ruined man, having lost all his money in an unfortunate speculation in an invention for the silvering of glass for the manufacture of mirrors. Some years before he died he had, on 11th January 1847, performed one operation which set him apart from other Westminster surgeons, the first operation in the hospital upon an anaesthetised patient. The anaesthetic was ether, given by a dentist, Mr Robinson of Gower Street. The patient was a woman suffering from venereal warts. She inhaled the ether vapour from Mr Robinson's apparatus for four minutes, and Hale Thomson shaved off the growths. It was a great success. Anaesthetics were first really developed at the hospital by another dental surgeon. This was Mr J. Chitty Clendon, the first dental surgeon to be appointed to the staff (1844), who published some of his cases, particularly the early ones where success was *not* obtained, such as the one on the Westminster School of Medicine porter, 'a little man, spare of habit' who inhaled the vapour for half an hour, until all the rooms in the house smelt of ether, without success. But the one Westminster man who really forwarded the science of anaesthesia in those times was John Snow (*see* Chapter 9). His studies, first with ether and later with chloroform, are a shining example of how to handle dangerous drugs with safety. It is a surprising thing that this man, whose studies on anaesthesia alone would have made him famous, was also far to the front in another field, that of the epidemiology of that deadly disease, cholera. Cholera

appeared in England at Sunderland in 1831, and at the age of 18 Snow in that year faced his first epidemic at Killingworth Colliery, near Newcastle. In 1849 a most severe epidemic struck London, so that in the week of 8th September, 2,021 people died of it but Westminster escaped. But in 1854 the hospital admitted 165 cases, of whom 12 died. It was the year of the epidemic in Broad Street, Golden Square. Snow, by meticulous questioning, established that the source of the infection was the contaminated water from the pump. It was a masterpiece of epidemiological study.

One of the protagonists of the fight against cholera in the hospital at this time was another old Westminster student, Dr William Richard Basham. He was a student in 1831 and graduated at Edinburgh in 1834. He was elected physician in 1843 and served the hospital as physician until 1877, when he had a stroke in the Board Room in June, lingering on to die in his old hospital in October. He was the third Westminster student to be elected to the staff as a physician (*see* Chapter 9).

By 1853, consequent on the necessity of absorbing the Medical School, considerable alterations were necessary. The operating theatre was moved from the ground floor to the second floor, being built out on a bracket between the two wings. The basement was rearranged to hold a mortuary, a post-mortem room and more space for out-patients, who had increased in numbers to 16,000 annually; a waiting room was cut off from the consulting room, and a dispensary, laboratory and surgery were also accom-

Dr John Snow as a young man, from a portrait in the possession of the family. (By permission of Dr S. P. W. Chave, London School of Hygiene and Medicine).

modated there. The ground floor was similarly re-arranged. The dispensary became the museum, and a library and reading room were formed from the old out-patients' room. Other such changes were made as it became apparent that the building was becoming too small for all its many functions.

As the different needs of the building changed, so did the staff. Anthony White had retired in 1846, and died in 1849, and in 1856 George James Guthrie, the last of the 'giants', a sad sufferer from chronic bronchitis and emphysema, died also. This great man had done much for the hospital and much also for the College of Surgeons where his reforming zeal had enabled him to remedy many abuses. His reforms specifically were directed to alleviate the lot of the Members as opposed to the Fellows. He is particularly remembered for the link he formed between the hospital and the Army medical services, to the officers of which he lectured for many years without fee. It was peculiarly fitting that when the Army in 1962 instituted a Guthrie Lecture and Medal, the first holder was another famous Westminster student and surgeon, Sir Stanford Cade. At Westminster he is remembered by the Guthrie Society, founded in 1887, at which every subject, 'save only politics and religion', may be the subjects of lecture, demonstration or discussion.

By 1860 the Board had to face the fact that necessary repairs and renovations would cost at least £4,000. They also faced the fact that in 1861, in spite of the opposition of the hospital chaplain, a powerful and active ladies committee had been formed, headed by

66

The Hospital in the Sanctuary

Lady Augusta Stanley. They were forced to build new nurses' bedrooms, to find room for a proper chapel (instead of unused wards) and to open Arden Ward as an obstetric ward so that the Maternity Charity, run in conjunction with the hospital, now had in-patients.

In this year, Frederic Bird was elected to the staff as the first obstetric physician, for it was the College of Physicians who first recognised obstetrics as a proper speciality. The Board, with much difficulty, managed to raise £1,900 by means of a dinner at Willis's Rooms and a special appeal 'on behalf of the poor low-lying and crowded Westminster, together with that part of Lambeth near Westminster Bridge' (for St Thomas's had not yet, of course, moved into that area). Westminster was changing its character as a city. Victoria Street had been cut in 1845, and shortly afterwards

The Night Porter's chair.

extensive building took place in the Pimlico area. The population was crowded, poor and contained many of Irish descent and extraction, whose riotous habits frequently mark (or mar) the hospital's history. In 1832, for example, 200 of them broke into the hospital to hold a wake over a man who had just died. On Christmas Day 1864, a worse incident occurred—another mob of Irish arrived with a woman, severely burnt. The surgery man, who was not sober, let them in, and they attacked the night porter, knocked him down, broke both bones of his leg by kicking him, and it required seven policemen to restore order. The steward was absent—his excuse was that he was too drunk to return to the hospital!

The Board remained obdurate to any suggestion that repairs and alterations should be carried out. By 1869 the figure for necessary repairs had reached £7,000 but they reduced it by half, even though a most damaging criticism of the hospital and its insanitary and misplaced water-closets had been published in the *British Medical Journal* (29th August 1868). Conditions continued to deteriorate. In 1874 it was found that there were 21 cases of erysipelas in the hospital, 14 of whom had become infected after admission. The walls and ceilings of the wards had not been whitewashed for two and a half years. The floors were washed twice a week but not polished. Dr de Havilland Hall recalled these evil times later: 'the old boards with gaping seams harbouring all kinds of germs which had to be kept clean by washing. How I used to pity the unfortunate patients on cleaning days, the atmosphere saturated with moisture from the damp boards'.

Of course, the water-closets were even more insanitary, were it possible, than ever. Finally, in 1875, a sub-committee was formed by Richard Davy, Surgeon to the Hospital, 1873–93. It reported that the following urgent reforms were necessary—

1. Removal of the water-closets from the wards.
2. An efficient hot-water system to be supplied to the wards.
3. The provision of many more baths (at this time there were only two baths in the hospital, both in the basement).
4. A general improvement of the cleanliness of the hospital.

Reaction by the Governors was considerable. A powerful body, headed by the President, the Duke of Westminster, urged rebuilding the hospital in Mill-bank. The scheme proposed was to build a hospital of 200 beds together with a medical school and nurses' home, all on one site. The site would have cost £10,000 and the cost of building £60,000. It was defeated.

The improvements to the hospital began in July 1877, and despite a builders' strike in August were finished by the third week in October. Mr Salter, the architect, solved the sanitary problem by applying to the corners of the building nine structures he called 'sanitary towers'. These can be clearly seen in the later pictures of the hospital. The three in the front of the hospital were octagonal and were decorated with Gothic gargoyles! They contained water-closets, pantries and bathrooms; as they had a narrow lobby each, this served for cross-ventilation. Mr Salter also added what amounted to an additional storey containing isolation wards, convalescent patients' day-rooms and new nurses' quarters approached by a private staircase. Finally, the wards throughout the hospital were refloored with teak, which could be polished and did not need washing. Unfortunately, the Governors refused to face the renovation of the main drainage, or to pass other items such as fixed hand-basins in the wards, and the establishment of a proper chapel. They limited the cost of repairs to £17,000 only. Yet these valuable alterations were not enough. In 1883 it was necessary to move the Medical School (*see* Chapter 9) elsewhere. This permitted enlargement of the Out-patient Department, and the placing of the post-mortem room on the roof; the museum and small surgery were turned into residents' bedrooms, and the surgery and side room took the place of the school library and the students' reading room. More nurses' bedrooms were constructed at the front of the building. Finally, the chapel was finished and consecrated in the spring of 1887. It cost £1,450, the total cost of all the improvements being £10,245. But they still left the drains untouched!

During all these structural alterations other important changes had, of course, taken place. The most important of these, the complete reform of the nursing services, is described in Chapter 10.

One man, particularly, paid a great part in these reforms. This was Sir Rutherford Alcock, K.C.B., D.C.L., F.R.C.S. He was born on 17th May 1809 at Ealing, and baptised next day as 'too delicate a baby to live'. Nevertheless, he became a pupil at the hospital

Sir Rutherford Alcock, K.C.B., D.C.L., F.R.C.S.

in 1827 and House Surgeon in 1829, when he joined the Army and saw service in Portugal and Spain. Resigning from the service in 1837 he studied surgery seriously and won the Jacksonian Prize twice, in 1839 and 1841. Severe rheumatism in the hands forced him to give up surgery, and from 1844 to 1871 he served with great distinction in the consular and diplomatic services in China and Japan, where he went as Envoy Extraordinary and Minister-Plenipotentiary in 1859. Here his conduct was so exemplary that the British Government created him K.C.B.

He organised the first exhibition of Japanese art in London in 1862, and, thus, is responsible, no doubt, as a source of inspiration for Gilbert and Sullivan's opera *The Mikado*. On retirement and his return to London he became a Governor and a moving force in the many committees of reform. No doubt his 'vigorous energy and bellicose individuality' were of great assistance to him. Such was the loyalty of old Westminster students to their hospital, a loyalty which gradually pervaded the whole staff in the later years of the century, that the scenes recorded earlier became unthinkable. The staff during this period contained many men of great worth, such as Dr Basham, Dr George Fincham and Charles Bland Ratcliffe. They were all good doctors and excellent teachers. Another also must be remembered, Dr Francis Edmund Anstie, an early lecturer in pathology, who died of septicaemia after pricking his finger at a post mortem. He had seemed destined for a brilliant career when he died in 1874. Then there was Dr Octavius Sturges, the founder of the Guthrie Society in 1887; he was so popular and beloved by

Dr Octavius Sturges, Founder of the Guthrie Society; Physician to Westminster 1865–94.

Dr Wm Murrell, Assistant-Physician to Westminster 1883–98; Physician 1898–1912. (Royal College of Physicians)

the staff and students alike that a ward was named after him when he died in 1894. The surgeons at this period included Mr Power, an eminent anatomist, and Barnard W. Holt, Anthony White's apprentice, a good surgeon and a lover of horses who retired early in 1873 and (says Heath) became proprietor of Newman's Livery Stables. Another surgeon at this time was Charles Brooke, F.R.S., who followed the sardonic

70

The Hospital in the Sanctuary

Benjamin Phillips, F.R.S. Mr Brooke invented a method of recording sunshine by photography, which was taken up at Greenwich Observatory: he was of an experimental turn of mind.

In 1877 there was appointed as Medical Registrar Dr William Murrell, who later got on the staff as Assistant Physician from 1883 to 1898 and Physician from 1898 to 1912. This solitary, shy man, while he was Registrar, introduced into medicine glyceryl trinitrate for the treatment of angina pectoris. It was a fundamental pharmacological advance that has brought relief to innumerable cardiac sufferers. Despite his oddities the students liked him: says Hereward, 'our affections were more likely to centre on Murrell. He was alleged to have a weak heart—in more ways than one—although this may have been an unwarranted slander. He always walked very slowly along the corridors and was a great adept in the writing of prescriptions . . .' He died of heart failure in 1912.

An unusual and pleasant 'Royal Occasion' occurred in 1879 when Prince Leopold and Princess Louise visited the hospital to see an exhibition of the art of William Morris, which was held in a ward containing convalescent patients. This must have been a great day for them!

There was appointed, in 1877 also, as Assistant Physician, Alexander Hughes Bennet, the first of four notable and famous neurologists associated with Westminster, the others being, of course, Sir James Purves Stewart, S. A. Kinnier Wilson, and S. P. Meadows.

This, then, was the hospital and the staff that the young Mr Byles found in the Queen's Jubilee Year of 1887, when he rode up on his penny-farthing bicycle from Westcombe Park to become a medical student. Yet before Mr Byles is followed to the Medical School in Caxton Street it would be as well to look at the history of the school and of the early history of the nursing staff so as to appreciate exactly what he found as a student in those days.

9

The Medical School in Its Early Years

'Mr William Pyle and Mr John Price . . . shall not . . . take
any cub or cubs.'

Westminster Hospital Minutes, Vol. 3, p. 400,
October 1733, 8th January 1733/34

The first mention of medical students, or 'cubs' as they were frequently called, is in 1734, when the Trustees on the 8th January 1733/34 recorded the following minute—

'Ordered that Mr William Pyle and Mr John Price or any succeeding Surgeon or Assistant Surgeon shall not have liberty to take any cub or cubs, or receive any fee or reward for admitting any persons to the practice of the Infirmary, their apprentices excepted.'

This rule was relaxed in 1737 when three 'cubs' were allowed to each surgeon, a number gradually increased until all limitations were removed. In 1738 a house pupil (resident) was allowed on condition that his 'master', Mr William Pyle, agreed to pay £12 for his board and lodging. The Apothecary was also allowed one resident pupil. 'Cubs' were at first regarded with suspicion and not allowed to remain in the infirmary in the absence of their master.

At this time medical students had two choices— they could attend the practice of the infirmary, paying a yearly or a perpetual fee to a physician or surgeon, or they could become apprentices to a surgeon. This involved the payment of a large sum of money in the order of £200 or more, but a place on the staff of the institution concerned was certain if the surgeon possessed any influence whatsoever. Thus, Mr Cheselden in 1703 was 'given apprentice to James Ferne surgeon for seven years from this date' (minute of the Barber-Surgeons Company). In 1710 he was admitted to the company (paying £10) and in 1711 he passed the company's examination, thus being entitled to practise surgery in London. He was unable to get on the staff at St Thomas's until July 1718 and he filled up

The Medical School in its Early Years

the interval by setting up a private anatomy school, probably the first of its kind in London. His course of lectures was published in 1713— *The Anatomy of the Human Body*, which by 1792 had reached its thirteenth edition. His example was followed by others, and in 1737 there were a dozen surgeons lecturing publicly on anatomy. Cheselden's lectures proved so popular that the Court of the Barber-Surgeons censured him for lecturing at the time of public lectures at the company's hall and for acquiring the bodies of male-factors before the company's beadles! He submitted, but the imposition rankled, and in 1745 the barbers and the surgeons were parted for ever, largely at his instigation.

It is a remarkable fact that anyone could practise and dispense medicine without passing any examina-tion whatsoever until the passage of the Apothecaries Act of 1815. After its passage, however, which neither the College of Physicians nor the College of Surgeons would assist or recommend, anyone not in practice before its passage who 'attended, prescribed and dis-penses medicine for gain in a Medical case' should be a Member of Licentiate of the Society of Apothecaries. He should also pass such an examination as the govern-ing body of the Society should propose. The Act gave the apothecaries power to prosecute and several Members of the Royal College of Surgeons were fined under its provisions. Those who intended a career in surgery would take the Membership of the Corpora-tion of Surgeons, which became the Royal College of Surgeons in 1800. Those intending a career as a con-sulting physician became a Licentiate of the College of Physicians and also took their M.D. degree, for without that they could not be made a Fellow of the Royal College.

The medical student of the day, therefore, received much of his tuition, not at the institution of his choice, but at private medical schools, such as that at Great Windmill Street where the Westminster surgeons taught. Here a student, hospital unknown, created a riot in 1810. He climbed to the roof and dropped a corpse's leg down the chimney next door, where it fell into a stewpan on the fire. On the return of the owner of the house this addition was discovered, and the mob that assembled would have torn the student apart had not his friends bribed them freely. Another private school was 'Tusons', Little Windmill Street, where Mr Guthrie lectured without fee for many years. He was a striking figure, very neat, and wore a large checked apron and armlets. In his clipped, offhand and military manner he gave the best lectures on surgery in his day. He was noted for the clearness of his delivery and the sound common sense of his teach-ing. Another well-known school was 'Dermotts' in Gerrard Street, over the Westminster Dispensary in Soho.

In those days students dissected fresh cadavers, which it was considered dangerous to dissect in the summer for fear of infection, but Joshua Brooks at Blenheim Street had discovered a way of preserving his 'specimens' and kept his school open all the year round. It was considered that each student needed two bodies to dissect for his course and one for practising operations. The demand far out-ran the legal supply,

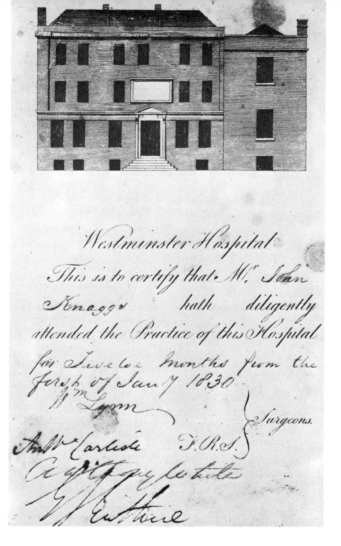

hence there was a regular market for the 'resurrection man' or 'body snatcher' until the Burke and Hare murders in Edinburgh and a similar series in London finally resulted in the passage of the Anatomy Act in 1832, which put them out of business.

Meanwhile, the College of Surgeons, concerned at the success of the private schools, passed a regulation in 1824 announcing that the College would accept certificates of proficiency in surgery only from certain universities, from teachers in medical schools attached to recognised London hospitals or from members of the honorary staffs of such hospitals. The pressure to establish a medical school at Westminster thus became compelling.

By 1826, Westminster Hospital had 100 beds, and there had been an increase in student fees. However, the Apothecary was later replaced by a clinical assistant to the physicians, and a dispenser. The clinical assistant was called the House Physician in 1834, the first holder being Dr Richard Basham. The perpetual fee for a physician's or surgeon's pupil was £21. The fee for a House pupil was 80 guineas, half of which went to the hospital for board and lodging, and pupils were now allowed to accompany the clinical assistant and House Surgeon in the wards; but there was still no medical school.

In 1833, Mr Dobson, Mr Crump, Dr Weatherhead, Dr Ryan and Dr Epps opened a 'Westminster School of Medicine' at No. 2 Prince's Street, Storey's Gate,

Pupil's Certificate of 1830, signed by Lynn, Carlisle, White and Guthrie.

ON

INJURIES OF THE HEAD

AFFECTING THE BRAIN:

AND

ON SOME POINTS

CONNECTED WITH

THE ANATOMY AND SURGERY

OF

INGUINAL AND FEMORAL HERNIÆ.

With Explanatory Plates.

BY

G. J. GUTHRIE, F.R.S.

*Presented to the Library of
the Westminster Hospital School of Medicine
by the Author
Octr 10th 1853*

A 205

Title page of Guthrie's Surgical Works (Medical School Library)

George James Guthrie, F.R.S., Founder of the Medical School 1834.

75

but it failed. In 1834, Mr Guthrie and Mr Hale Thompson with Dr Robert Bentley Todd and John Burne, opened a school in Dean Street (roughly about the Victoria Street end of Great Smith Street). They were joined by some of the staff from the 1833 school and paid for the cost of the building, some £3,000, themselves. The project was supported by several of the Governors but at a special Board Meeting in September 1834 a proposal to obtain both the patronage of the Governors and the permission to call the school the 'Westminster School of Medicine' was defeated by 53 votes to 34. The hospital physicians, Dr Hamilton Roe and Sir George Tuthill, opposed the scheme (they had a plan for a school of their own which came to naught). Not surprisingly, the aged Mr Lynn voted against it, as did the rest of the staff. Many of the Governors and the Treasurer were in favour. However, on 1st October Mr Guthrie delivered the introductory lecture, and did so for four years, when he was succeeded by Mr Benjamin Phillips, F.R.S., who became Assistant Surgeon to the hospital in 1843, and was Surgeon from 1843 to 1856. In 1841 the Governors finally noted the 'paramount importance of a school of medicine in connexion with the Hospital'. It may be noted, in parenthesis, that the school was doing well and that the *Lancet* in 1838 had stated, 'This School is now united with the Westminster Hospital, where clinical lectures are given by the physicians and surgeons'. The Governors had also given the students the porter's day room, the stone floor of which had been boarded over, as a museum and reading room. It was at the west end of the base-

ment corridor. Smoking, drinking and card playing were forbidden. It would seem that Dr Basham revived the idea of adopting the Dean Street School on 10th May 1840. By 8th September 1840 a Quarterly and special General Board minuted the following:

'This Board, having taken into consideration the resolution of the House Committee of the 25th August last, in reference to a Westminster School of Medicine, it is moved by Mr Ayrton, seconded by Mr Anthony White.

Resolved:

'That it is expedient in conformity to the usage of all the great Metropolitan Hospitals and most of the Provincial Hospitals of any magnitude, that this Institution should have a School of Medicine attached to it under the name of the Westminster School of Medicine, to be under the control of the Governors, but not to involve the Charity in any expense, or any pecuniary responsibility whatever, and that a special Committee of the Physicians and Surgeons to the Hospital together with five Governors be appointed for the purpose of carrying this resolution into effect.'

The difficulty now arose of financing the purchase of the Dean Street School. Three physicians and three surgeons each guaranteed £50 in two instalments. £1,600 was needed with the furniture at a valuation. However, this was finally agreed on by 29th June 1841, but the vendors inserted a betterment clause in

The Medical School in its Early Years

case of a compulsory purchase under a contemplated Westminster improvements scheme, i.e. the construction of Victoria Street. They insisted that if more than £1,600 was paid in compensation, then they should be compensated up to a maximum of £900. On this, the Dean and Chapter of the Abbey promptly bid £2,500 for the property and the school was forced to pay this sum to acquire it, plus, of course, the extra for the fittings, a total of £2,913. Subscriptions had brought in £1,413 and the rest raised on mortgage (at an interest of £75 per year).

By this time there was a grave falling off in students from 55 in Guthrie's day, to 21. It was general over the Metropolis, even St Thomas's had only a few students. Dr Robert Hunter of Glasgow had paid £100 to become Lecturer in Anatomy and had also the considerable expense of transferring his specimens and paying his anatomy demonstrator £50 a year. On 4th November he wrote to the committee: 'three weeks of the Session have elapsed and the vestige of a class has scarcely yet been formed', and asked the committee what they were going to do as he was seriously out of pocket. The School of Medicine Committee could only pass the following resolution. They had 'no doubt of the School's ultimate success and would give their best consideration to any proposition which the Lecturers might recommend to meet the difficulties'. This resolution, no doubt, was accompanied by some action on the part of the other lecturers, for Dr Hunter struggled with adversity and a continuing scarcity of students and, on 9th July 1843, sold half his interest to J. E. Ericksen, who finally bought him out completely in 1846. Dr Hunter resigned his lectureship on 3rd July 1846 and was succeeded by Ericksen who taught anatomy and physiology, practical anatomy being taught, first by Mr Pennell and, later, by Mr Holt. When the session of 1846–57 opened on 1st October the school suffered a serious blow, for the Council of the Royal College of Surgeons, after due inspection, refused to recognise the anatomy lectures. This was because Dr Hunter had taken away most of his anatomical specimens, and what was left was insufficient to illustrate the anatomy lectures, the students studying anatomy having to attend King's College. The final *coup de grâce* came on 19th October 1846. The Commissioners of the Westminster Improvements executed a compulsory purchase of the 'pretty Gothic premises' in Dean Street for £3,150, exclusive of fixtures, and paid this sum on 5th December. The mortgage and other outstanding liabilities were discharged. The medical officers and lecturers recovered their contributions, the balance being invested in the purchase of £584 8s. 9d. of 3 per cent Consols, but the school thus came to a dismal end *pro tem*. What happened to the school in 1847 is not recorded, but on 17th February 1848 a committee of Governors and medical men, consisting of the Treasurer, Pleydell-Bouverie, four other governors, the Senior Physician, Dr Hamilton Roe, with the Senior Surgeon, Mr Phillips, met to consider the position. They recommended that the school should be re-established and, eventually, in June 1849, took a lease of premises in Westminster Mews behind the hospital. The lease, from the Commissioners of

WESTMINSTER HOSPITAL

SCHOOL OF MEDICINE,

SESSION 1849-50.

The Session will commence on MONDAY, OCTOBER 1st, 1849, with an
Introductory Lecture, at 4 p.m., by DR. HAMILTON ROE.

HOSPITAL PRACTICE.

Daily, from Twelve to Two.

This Hospital affords relief to 2,000 In-Patients, and 14,000 Out-Patients, Annually.

Consulting Physician ....DR. BRIGHT.   *Consulting Surgeon*...Mr. GUTHRIE.

Physicians .... { DR. HAMILTON ROE,   *Surgeons* .... { Mr. LYNN,
                           DR. KINGSTON,   Mr. HALE THOMSON,
                           DR. BASHAM.   Mr. BENJ. PHILLIPS.

Assistant Surgeon ...... Mr. BARNARD HOLT.

Clinical Lectures will be delivered regularly, twice a-week, by the Physicians and Surgeons.

Post Mortem Examinations will be made under the superintendence of the Physicians and Surgeons: on which occasions, Pathological Demonstrations will be given, to illustrate the structural changes effected by disease.

FEES FOR ATTENDANCE.

MEDICAL PRACTICE:—	£. s. d.	SURGICAL PRACTICE:—	£. s. d.
Six Months	10 10 0	Three Months	8 8 0
Twelve Months	12 12 0	Six Months	12 12 0
Eighteen Months	15 15 0	Twelve Months	21 0 0
Perpetual	21 0 0	Perpetual	31 10 0

Conjoint Fee, for the period of Hospital Practice required by the Royal College of Surgeons and the Society of Apothecaries, Twenty-six Guineas.

MATERNITY CHARITY.

Physicians.—DR. FREDERIC BIRD and DR. W. MERRIMAN.

Surgeon.—Mr. GREENHALGH.

This Charity affords attendance to 500 Lying-in Patients, Annually.

Clinical Lectures will be delivered by Mr. GREENHALGH.

Westminster Hospital 1716–1974

Woods and Forests was for forty years at a rent of £60 per annum. £700 was spent on converting these stables and outhouses into a medical school, and the following staff were recruited on 29th June 1849:

Dr Hamilton Roe	Medicine
Dr Herman Lewis	Chemistry
Dr Basham	Materia Medica
Dr Frederic Bird and	
Dr Merriman	Midwifery
Mr C. Brook and Mr Hillman	Physiology
Mr Carsten Holthouse	Anatomy
Mr Benjamin Phillips	Surgery
Mr Clendon	Dentistry
Dr Radcliffe	Botany

Dr Fincham, Dr Greenhalgh and Dr Tanner also lectured and a Demonstrator in anatomy was appointed for £20.

The School Prospectus makes no mention of a Dean, and all the business side, payment of fees, etc. was in the hands of the Hospital Secretary, Mr F. J. Wilson. It may be noted that the General Fee to all the lectures required by the Royal College of Surgeons and Society of Apothecaries was forty guineas, exclusive of Practical Chemistry, an extra five guineas.

To finance the school the lecturers paid into the school fund an amount equal to the value of their chair, e.g. the Chair of Anatomy was worth £25, later raised to £35. 'Hard', says Mr Carsten Holthouse, 'to myself especially, who was the largest contributor.' The members of the hospital staff paid one-third of

78

Front page of the 1849–50 Medical School Prospectus.

The Medical School in its Early Years

the fees they received from their pupils only. Furthermore, to get students at all it was decreed that students entering the hospital practice alone could attend the lectures free. Thus, thirty students were gathered together, and Dr Hamilton Roe gave the introductory lecture on 1st October. Another bitter blow was struck on 10th November when another letter from the Royal College of Surgeons arrived stating that the College could not recognise the school, 'owing to the deficiencies in the Museum'. In this dark hour Mr Lane offered to take the pupils once more to King's College, and Mr Holthouse offered to make good the deficiency in specimens by the end of the year provided a sum of £30 was put at his disposal. It was granted, he was appointed Curator and by much hard work he succeeded. By the end of December 1849 the Museum passed a searching examination by Mr Arnold and Mr Caesar Hawkins for the Council of the College, and recognition was granted. As the lectures in 1851–52 were *not* free, the number of students began to decline, and in 1851 twelve months notice was given to terminate the lease as the Government wished to build on the site (the Stationery Office). In 1852, therefore, school buildings were constructed at the back of the hospital, the cost, £918 10s. 0d., paid, *mirabile dictu*, by the hospital! However, it was too little and too late (almost), for in 1853–54 there were only five entries!

By this time Mr Holthouse had been lecturing for five years without remuneration or without any return for the money he had advanced in 1849; he thereupon resigned. It was a very courageous and salutary move. He frankly told the committee that the standard of accommodation for students must be improved, and that until this was done, larger intakes of students could not be expected. The committee then appointed him sole manager of the school with *carte blanche* to effect such improvements as he thought fit and to draw up the prospectus for the next year. This needed the hospital's sanction and the expenditure of money.

The sanction was given, the financial assistance was refused. By some devious but unrevealed method Holthouse succeeded in his plans, improvements were effected, and in 1854–55 there were fifteen full students, in 1855–56 there were seventeen, and the school continued at the back of the hospital without a break until its removal to Caxton Street in 1885. In 1856 Christopher Heath was appointed Demonstrator in Anatomy, his vigorous demonstrations drawing students from all over London. He said he, 'did not know where the Hospital was', when he came to see about the post, but he left his mark on it, both as a teacher of anatomy and of operative surgery. He left, in 1866, to become Surgeon to University College Hospital. An histology laboratory was built in 1874 and that, and the chemistry laboratories, were enlarged in 1878. But it was plain that the school needed more room, as did the hospital, for much needed improvements; many sites were considered but there was still some sluggishness of thought to contend with in the governing body. However, vigorous action began in 1883, a site next to St James's Park station in Caxton Street was purchased for £4,500, and the foundation stone was laid by the Duke of Westminster on 28th February 1885.

The new medical school was said to be built in the Tudor style, a fact that will surprise all that ever saw or worked on it. Together with the site the total cost was £13,815. To this sum the Board of Governors of the Hospital gave £3,000 and the Lecturers £1,000; a generous sum of 1,000 guineas was given by the Common Council of the City of London: a sum of £7,791 collected for the hospital and the school was divided so that the school received £5,843, i.e. three-fourths. The balance of £4,000 was raised as a mortgage at 4 per cent. The collections of funds for the school and for the renovations in the hospital at this time was inaugurated by a dinner at Willis's Rooms in 1883, presided over by the Patron to the Hospital, H.R.H. The Prince of Wales. In his speech he said: 'The medical school buildings are inconvenient and too small . . . . The utmost has been made of the space belonging to the Hospital and there is only one way in which the improvements in question can be carried out—namely, by buying a small site near the Hospital.' This dinner raised some £2,000, the list was headed by Queen Victoria who gave 20 guineas, and the Prince of Wales himself gave 100 guineas.

The new school and the renovated hospital are described in Chapter 11, but it is instructive to look back and see what sort of medical men were produced by the hospital, both before and after the introduction of a medical school. Between 1734 and 1838 the following surgeons, all pupils or apprentices to men on the staff were elected Surgeons to the Hospital: J. V. Sheldon, F.R.S., William Lynn (P.R.C.S., 1825), Sir Anthony Carlisle, F.R.S. (P.R.C.S., 1828, 1837), Anthony White (P.R.C.S., 1834, 1841), William Bewicke Lynn and F. Hale Thomson. There were two physicians, W. G. Maton, F.R.S. and John Ayrton Paris (P.R.C.P. 1844 to 1856). Six surgeons and two physicians. Between 1838 and 1938 we find the following students were elected to the staff:

APOTHECARIES' HALL.

Mr. *John Snow*   *4 Feb* 1838
of full age,

ndidate for a Certificate of Qualification.

of *William Snow of York Merchant*

APPRENTICE to Mr. *William Hardcastle Newcastle on Tyne*

APOTHECARY for *six* Years.

ENTURE DATED *22 June 1827*

TIMONIAL of MORAL CHARACTER. *Dr. Warburton*

Bap *15 March 1813*

LECTURES commenced. *Oct 1836*

2 COURSES ON CHEMISTRY. *Lane*

3 —————— MATERIA MEDICA. *Epps*

2 —————— ANATOMY and PHYSIOLOGY. ?

2 —————— ANATOMICAL DEMONSTRATIONS. *Lucas Jones Savage*

—————— BOTANY. *Epps*

2 —————— PRINCIPLES and PRACTICE of MEDICINE. *Ryan — Venables*

—————— FORENSIC MEDICINE. *Epps*

2 —————— MIDWIFERY. *Jewel*

PRACTICAL CHEMISTRY.

MORBID ANATOMY.

2 MONTHS' ATTENDANCE at *Westmr Hos*

EXAMINED by *Mr Smith Saffeard*

John Snow. Certificate of Attendance.

Dr John Snow, Anaesthetist and Epidemiologist.
(Wellcome Museum)
Primus inter pares, nec pluribus impar

C. J. Guthrie, B. W. Holt, George E. Legg Pearse, A. H. Evans, Sir E. Rock Carling, Stanley Dodd, Sir Stanford Cade, Sir Clement Price Thomas and E. Stanley Lee—Surgeons to Westminster Hospital. There were also elected in this time two physicians, W. R. Basham and Dr Gossage, one dermatologist, H. Thompson Barron, one anaesthetist, R. Machray, a radiotherapist Dr F. M. Allchin and a radiologist Dr W. H. Coldwell. It is curious that since Dr Gossage was elected in 1895 no Westminster student has been Physician to the Hospital until September 1965, when Dr Brian Gibberd was elected.

Joseph Thomas Clover, F.R.C.S., 1825–82, sometime Anaesthetist to Westminster Hospital. (Royal College of Surgeons)

However, the worth of the institution is perhaps better represented by old students like Sir Rutherford Alcock, the surgeon diplomat, or by John Snow, the anaesthetist and epidemiologist, without doubt one of the most brilliant students produced by this or any other medical school. John Snow was born on 15th March 1813 at York. He was the eldest son of a farmer. At the age of fourteen he was apprenticed to a medical man William Hardcastle of Newcastle-upon-Tyne. In 1831 he was sent to Killingworth Colliery where an epidemic of cholera had broken out. He came to London in 1836, first travelling to Liverpool, then walking through North Wales to Bath, and thence onwards to London! He studied at the Great Windmill School 1836–37, and from 1837 to 1838 he studied clinical subjects at the Westminster Hospital. In May 1838 he became M.R.C.S., in October L.S.A.; M.B. (London) in 1843 and M.D. in 1844. He was a man of slight constitution and was believed early in life to have tuberculosis; in 1845 signs of renal disease appeared, but he recovered (thanks to Dr Bright). In 1846 he took up anaesthesia and become the first man to study the subject really scientifically, first ether and later, chloroform (no man can have handled this latter drug so well). He is said to have given 4,000 chloroform anaesthetics without a death. He gave chloroform to Queen Victoria on 7th April 1853 at the birth of Prince Leopold, also on 14th April 1857 on the birth of Princess Beatrice, ('that blessed chloroform', wrote the Queen).

Between these royal occasions, however, came his famous intervention in the cholera epidemic of 1854 in

The Medical School in Its Early Years

the Broad Street, Golden Square, area. Having satisfied himself that all the afflicted (and there were 89 deaths in this epidemic) had used water from the pump, he persuaded the Vestry officials to remove the pump handles: this was done on 9th September, the epidemic rapidly subsiding. Dr John Snow fell ill on 9th June 1858 while correcting the proofs of his book, *On Chloroform and Other Anaesthetics* and died on 17th June at the age of forty-five. He is buried in Brompton Cemetery.

His place as the premier anaesthetist in London was taken by Mr Joseph Clover, from Norfolk and University College Hospital. He took his F.R.C.S. in 1850 and completed his training as a surgeon but became increasingly devoted to the new science of anaesthesia. He anaesthetised Queen Alexandra (when Princess of Wales), King Leopold of the Belgians, and the exiled Emperor Napoleon III. The Hospital staff were honoured to have this eminent man associated with them. He lives on as the inventor of Clover's crutch, used for many years to maintain a patient in the lithotomy position, and Clover's ether inhaler which was still in use in the 1930s.

It might be thought, again, that the typical Westminster man was represented by Sir George S. Robertson, K.C.S.I., I.M.S., who had won an Exhibition in Anatomy in 1873. He joined the Indian Medical Service in 1878 and, after seeing service in the Afghan war of 1879–80, became involved with the Indian Foreign Department. In 1889 with a small force he was besieged in the fort at Chitral where he held out until relieved, six weeks later. He was created

Student's Prize Medals won by T. Rutherford Adams 1858–59.

K.C.S.I. in 1895, retired from the I.M.S. in 1899, and entered Parliament as M.P. for Central Bradford in 1906. Perhaps a more typical man was Thomas Rutherford Adams, who won the medals illustrated above in 1858–59. He became House Surgeon in 1861, received his M.D. later, and lived and practised in Croydon for many years. How his medals came to be discovered in a house that was being demolished at Tooting has yet to be elucidated.

The Nursing Profession, 1720–1887

'. . . to allow them nurses . . .' (Charitable Proposal for
relieving the Sick and Needy and other Distressed Persons)
Preface to Westminster Hospital Minutes, Vol. 1, 1715/16

When the Charitable Society for Relieving the Sick
and Needy made its first staff appointment it was that
of Mrs Jane Alden (or Aldin) to be Matron. She,
therefore, is the first member of that long line of
Matrons and nurses which has served Westminster
until the present day. The day was 30th December
1719, three months before the infirmary was opened.
The first nurse was Ann Squire, hired at £5 14s. per
year, which was raised by one shilling a week after
3rd August on Mrs Alden's request. This wage, of
course, was in addition to board and lodging. Shortly
afterwards she left and was followed by Margaret
Cunningham, who was nurse to the infirmary until
22nd February 1722, when: 'Mary Cowley and
Margaret Black returned thanks for their cure and
are discharged—and Margaret Cunningham, the
nurse to this Infirmary being taken ill and made
incapable of attending the business of the House:

'Ordered that she be admitted Inpatient and that
Margaret Black be entertained as nurse to the
Infirmary at the rate of eleven shillings a month to
be paid the first day of every month.'

It sounds a strange way of recruiting staff, but
Margaret Black served the infirmary well until 26th
November 1729 when she was discharged and forbidden to enter it again, for disobedience to the
Matron. By this time, of course, the infirmary had
moved to Chapel Street. On 5th January 1730 the
Trustees laid down rules as to the diet of the patients
and the staff. Each servant of the House was to have
1 lb of meat a day, one loaf of bread of 16 oz and
three pints of small beer. It is to the credit of the
Board that when the amount of meat was cut to 8 oz
for the patients in March 1734, that of the nurses was
not cut. There were two nurses now, for a night nurse

The Nursing Profession, 1720–1887

was engaged in August 1733. Indeed, the nurses' (and other servants') food was increased, they being allowed 3 oz of butter or cheese in addition. A further order specifically stated that night nurses were to have one pint of ale for breakfast. One wonders whether this rule was ever rescinded! When the infirmary finally moved to James Street the list of quarterly salaries reads as follows—

26th March 1735

The Apothecary to Lady Day	£5	0s. 0d.
The Matron to the same time	£3	0s. 0d.
The Messenger	£2	0s. 0d.
A quarter's wages to Nurse Hale	£1	15s. 0d.
A quarter's wages to Nurse Ashley	£1	15s. 0d.
A quarter's wages to Nurse Lloyd	£1	15s. 0d.
A Month's salary to Nurse Jenkins		11s. 8d.

There were thus four nurses, two day and two night. The Matron mentioned above is Mrs Elizabeth Owen, the second matron, for Mrs Alden had resigned on account of ill health on 23rd May 1734 with a gratuity of £2 2s. 0d. and the special thanks of the Board for her long and most admirable services. It is a pleasure to think that the Board thought so highly of Mrs Alden. Even in the dissensions that led to the formation of St George's Hospital the Board found time to purchase a 'Matt' for the Matron's room, and even when the medical staff left at that time she remained faithful to her post and trust. Nurses at this time were engaged on a month's notice and that is why in the above list of staff, Nurse Jenkins was paid but one month's salary—she was under notice having

THE MATRONS OF WESTMINSTER HOSPITAL

1719–1898

Mrs Jane Alden	1719–1734, resigned
Mrs Elizabeth Owen	1734–1741, dismissed
Mrs Lydia Williams	1741–1746, died
Mrs Gregory	1746–1761, died
Mrs Catherine Callowhill	1761–1769, died
Mrs Amy Baildon	1769–1771, died
Mrs Mary Turner	1771–1794, died
Mrs Mortteras	1794–1818, retired
Mrs F. Cox	1818–1847, died
Miss Elizabeth Eager	1847–1871, retired
Miss Charlotte Spencer	1871–1872, died
Mrs M. E. Barber	1872–1873, resigned
Miss Elizabeth Merryweather	1873–1880, died
Miss M. J. Pyne	1880–1898, retired

been found 'much disguised in drink'. This was, alas, a not uncommon cause for dismissal in those days. The Board made even more stringent regulations to prevent the import of gin into the infirmary, for this was the time when gin (Geneva, as it was called) was exceedingly cheap. The governments of the day had thrown open the distilling trade and put far too light a tax on spirits. The idea was to encourage the growth of corn! It was not until 1751 when a severe tax on gin was introduced that conditions improved and the baptisms in the London area finally exceeded

A Quarterly Bill, March 1735.

great temptation for the relatively well-fed nurses to try to smuggle out of the infirmary food, soap, candles and the like. This meant that the Matron had to be as vigilant as a hawk, for she was responsible for such items, in addition to other duties. It was this which led to the dismissal of the second Matron, Mrs Owen, in 1741. Having served the infirmary very well, her wages were raised to £16 in 1737, which showed that the Board had confidence in her. In 1741, after a long investigation, a special committee found extensive neglect and waste and the Matron was dismissed. It will be seen from the table on p. 85 that the next five matrons from 1741 to 1794 all died, mostly of fevers caught in the infirmary, as did many nurses. Nursing was then a hard life and a good nurse was hard to find.

In 1742 there was considerable anti-Roman-Catholic feeling and the staff were investigated as to their religious beliefs. A rule was passed that any member of the staff found, 'to profess the Romish religion on or before June 21st' would be dismissed. Unfortunately, the cook, Margaret Humphreys, and one of the nurses, Nurse Martin, were found to be Roman Catholics. The cook was forthwith dismissed but the Board were obviously unhappy about Nurse Martin. She was given notice of dismissal but a gratuity of £20 was to be given her 'for her good and faithful service'. During the month's notice, however, she was seen to receive Communion according to the Anglican rites. The Board rescinded the order of dismissal and also the £20 gratuity. But even in those days other people noted the excellence of Westminster

the burials! It is against this background that the tendency of drunkenness among the poorer classes, and the nurses of those days came from the poorer classes, must be judged. Furthermore, there was a

nurses. In 1743 the London Hospital wrote praising the excellence of a nurse who had been in service at Westminster. The Board was pleased and sent the London Hospital twenty-five copies of a recent anniversary sermon for their edification. As the number of beds increased, so did the number of nurses (*see* table below).

NURSES AND BEDS OVER THE YEARS

Date	Beds	Day Nurses	Night Nurses	Total	Wages/year
1720/24	12–18	1	—	1	£5 6s.
1724/34	15–31	1	1	2	£6 10s.
1735	35	2	2	4	£7
1745	86	6	5	11	£7–£7 10s.
1791	86	8	4	12	£8
1800	90	6	4	10	£8 8s.
1839	106	12	4	16	£12–£18

1880   190 beds, 7 Sisters, 12 day nurses, 1 night Sister, 6 night nurses—up to 25 probationers.

1939   420 beds, 24 Sisters, 72 nurses, 12 in preliminary training school.

Westminster Hospital Group

1965   1,090 beds, 1,200 nurses, 542 in preliminary training school.

1973   1,564 beds, 1,675 nurses, 680 in basic training courses.

An order of 1759 gives an illuminating view on the qualities the Board were looking for:

Nurses must be unmarried (without children). They must be under forty-five when appointed. A month's

trial was to be obligatory. They were required to behave with respect and decency, to see that patients took their medicine and to look after the diet of the patients. They were to inform the Matron immediately when a patient died. They were further strictly forbidden (the penalty being instant dismissal) to take money or other gifts from the patients or to carry out provisions from the infirmary, or to take spiritous liquors. Finally, once discharged they could not be re-employed.

On the opening of the hospital in the Sanctuary each ward of the group of three (*see* diagram below) was given a day nurse, and each group of three had

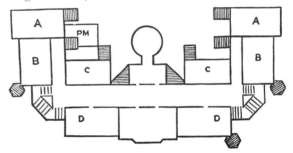

Ground plan of the Hospital in the Sanctuary (from Langdon-Davies).

one night nurse. The day nurses had each a little room cut off from the ward. Conditions, however, gradually improved in spite of the determined opposition of the medical staff led by Dr Basham. Mr George Cowell, Surgeon to Westminster Hospital 1873–96, writing in 1899 says—

'Hospital Committees in those days were not so liberal as they are now and all increase of wages was absolutely refused for many years. . . . Westminster had gradually come to be nursed by a lower and lower class . . . in spite of the determined opposition of the then senior physician, Dr Basham, a change was made and the cost of the nursing was doubled at a bound.'

Dr F. de Havilland Hall, Physician to Westminster 1894–1912 (he qualified in 1868 at St Bartholomew's) said, in 1899—

'Even when I was House Physician in 1872 I had to take all the temperatures myself, and it never entered my head that a nurse would be capable of taking and recording temperatures. This may be taken as a typical instance of the advance in nursing. The pleasing costume, scrupulously clean and neat, of the nurses of today is in marked contrast to the dark stuff and often untidy dresses of the past generation of nurses!!'

Even before Miss Nightingale had begun her great work, Miss Elizabeth Eager, Matron from 1847 to 1873, had begun a marked improvement in conditions at Westminster. She was the first to use the term 'trained nurse'. She wished to put a trained nurse, a 'Sister' in charge of each group of three wards with one nurse for each ward (of ten or eleven patients) under her. The staff and the Board disliked the term 'Sister' and in 1853 managed to introduce the term 'Head Nurse' (see current American practice). The

hours of duty were fixed at 6 a.m. to 10 p.m. for Head Nurses, and night nurses (called assistant nurses) worked from 8.30 p.m. to 12.30 a.m. and from 12.30 a.m. to 5.30 p.m. It was in 1853 that the Sisterhood of St John obtained permission to have their probationers undergo instruction at the hospital, at which to this day members of the Order of St John and of the British Red Cross still attend for short courses.

When Miss Nightingale and her party of nurses sailed for Scutari in October 1854, at least two Westminster nurses accompanied her. In a letter from Miss Nightingale dated from Scutari 13th August and read to the House Committee on 4th September, one of them, Miss Mary Tattersall, is mentioned. She desired to forward £5 for the hospital, 'being the first money she had earned' which she wished to give to the place where she had received so much kindness. The other, Mary Ann Noble, had to return from Scutari on account of her health. Miss Nightingale had given her an excellent testimonial, so the House Committee appointed her Head Nurse of the Queen Adelaide group of female wards. This was 1st January 1856. It was very largely the Ladies Committee, led by Lady Augusta Stanley, the wife of Dean Stanley, who forced the Governors to alter their stubborn attitude to the problem of the nursing services in the hospital. When Miss Eager retired in 1871 she was succeeded by Miss Spencer who, unfortunately, died shortly afterwards. At the recommendation of Dr Basham, Mrs Barber was appointed. By this time (in 1870) a distinctive uniform had finally been adopted. A Nursing sub-committee was formed to confer with Mrs Barber on

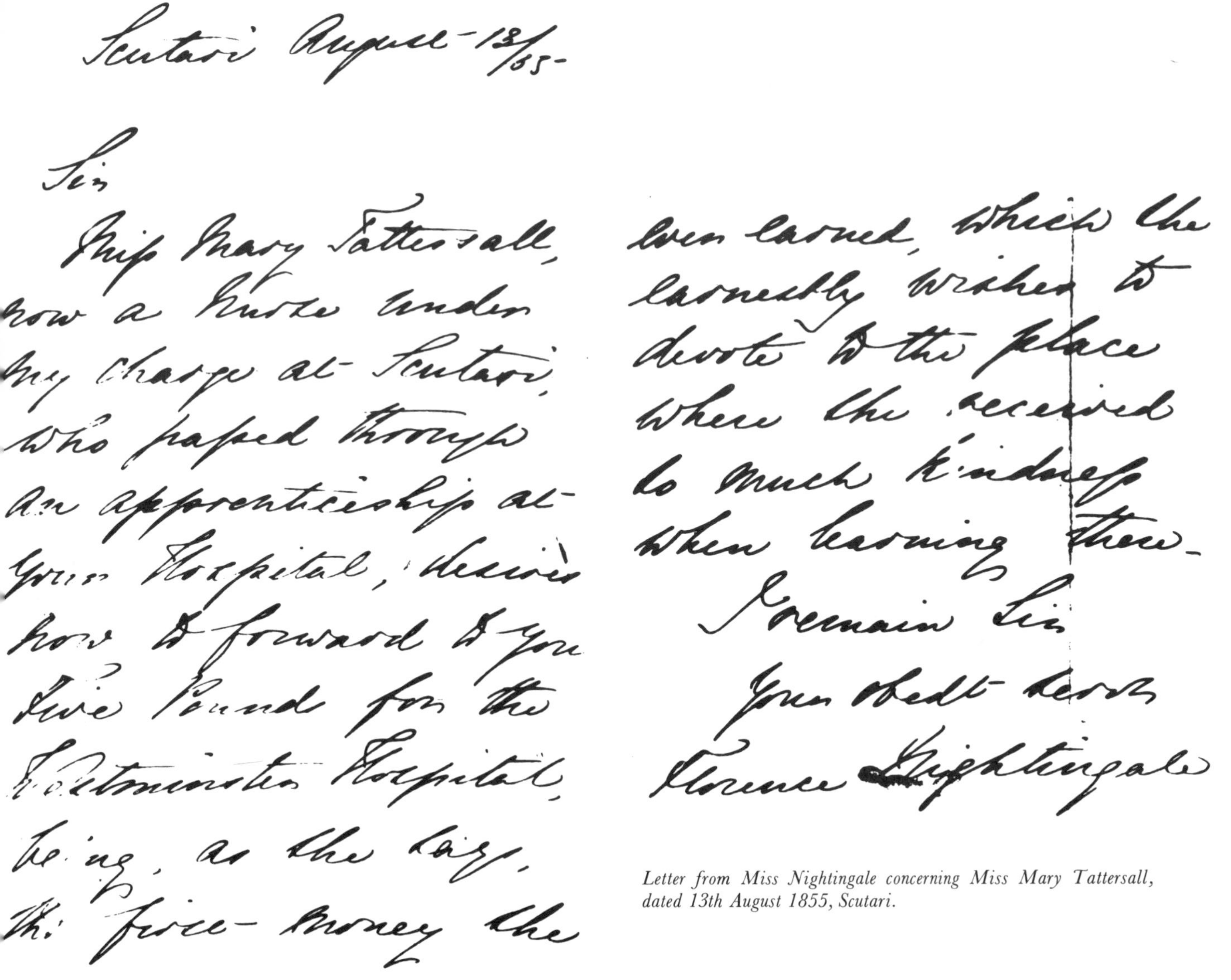

Scutari August 13/55—

Sir,

Miss Mary Tattersall, now a Nurse under my charge at Scutari, who passed through an apprenticeship at your Hospital, desires now to forward to you Five Pound for the Westminster Hospital, being, as the last, this five-money she has earned, which she earnestly wishes to devote to the place where she received so much kindness when learning there—

I remain Sir

Your obedt Servt

Florence Nightingale

Letter from Miss Nightingale concerning Miss Mary Tattersall, dated 13th August 1855, Scutari.

Lady Augusta Stanley c.1870.

90

Nurses in Uniform 1951.

The Nursing Profession, 1720–1887

the management and general control of the nurses. This committee (aided by a memorandum from Lady Augusta Stanley) produced several definite recommendations concerning hours of duty, special uniforms for Head Nurses and assistant nurses (they pointed out that a Head Nurse's dress would cost about 10s. 7d. and an assistant nurse's about 9s. and that two dresses a year would be needed). A nurses' dining room with fixed meal times and other material things, such as furniture, should be provided. They did not, however, as Langdon-Davies points out, mention anything about the necessity for training the nurses in their duties!

A further committee under Sir Rutherford Alcock was therefore set up in 1872 to report on this point, especially as regard the systems of nursing employed at other hospitals. In 1873 the committee reported its findings. The system then in use cost £7 18s. per bed per year and was not satisfactory. Hospitals such as King's College Hospital, where the nursing was under the St John's Sisterhood, who provided the staff for an agreed sum, were more efficient but the cost was £13 15s. a bed per year. A third scheme was that developed at the Liverpool Royal Infirmary. At this institution there was a training school for nurses under the charge of a lady superintendent who provided the nurses required for the infirmary for a fixed sum, including board, wages and uniforms. This scheme was run by two sisters, Miss Mary and Miss Elizabeth Merryweather.

The committee were much impressed by this scheme and the Misses Merryweather were invited to come

Bouverie Ward. Sister Elizabeth Christian wearing the badge of the Order of St Katherine.

and take over the nursing, which they accepted. Dr Basham pointed out the injustice to Mrs Barber but was overruled. She was dismissed with the thanks of the Board and a financial consideration (one year's salary—£300). When this happened six nurses immediately resigned and had to be replaced by Liverpool-trained nurses. Miss Mary Merryweather was engaged as Lady Superintendent at £80 a year from 4th March 1873; her sister was appointed Matron from 1st May. Storms ensued, and all Sir Rutherford Alcock's diplomatic skill was needed to keep the peace between Miss Elizabeth Merryweather and the committee. The Nurses' Training School, after beginning its career in a house in Great Smith Street, finally took up its quarters at 27 Queen Anne's Gate in May 1874 and the hospital agreed to pay £8 a bed a year for 190 beds with a return of £25 a nurse a year for board. This scheme only worked because of the close link between the two sisters, and when, in 1880, Miss Mary died, her sister resigned her post also. It was then possible to combine the two posts of Matron and Lady Superintendent. A permanent establishment of seven day-ward sisters and six night nurses, was set up. The Home could also send up to twenty-five probationers for training. A Nursing joint committee was also appointed to take care of disputes between the medical officers and the Matron-Superintendent on nursing matters.

It was on these terms that Miss Pyne became Matron in 1880 and nursing became free to develop its own professional skills and disciplines. Seven years later Queen Victoria called in Sir Rutherford Alcock. She wished to celebrate her Jubilee Year by decorating some deserving nurses by appointing them to the old Royal Foundation of St Katherine. Sir Rutherford Alcock with the assistance of Sir James Paget and the Duke of Westminster drew up the regulations. The recipients received £50 per annum for three years over and above their salary and the school they belonged to received the same amount. The holders were given a badge to be worn on the left arm—an oval of white surrounded by a border of bright green, with the letters St.K. in gold. The first three recipients were Miss Elizabeth Christian, Sister of King William, Bouverie and Burdett Wards, Miss Lucy King, Arden and Hallett Wards, and Miss Eva Kent, Hollond and Chadwick Wards. The picture (p. 91) shows Bouverie Ward with Sister Elizabeth Christian in the left forefront wearing her badge.

From their training school, nurses would travel to all parts of the world taking with them their skills and the name of their hospital, Westminster. It is said that a Tsar of Russia, so impressed by their abilities decreed that a Westminster nurse in uniform needed no passport to travel anywhere in his vast domains. They were, in the future, to nurse two kings of England. Sister Nellie Purdie, M.B.E. had the honour to nurse H.M. George V in his severe illness in 1928–29, and the names of those who nursed H.M. George VI are to be seen on the King's window in the Chapel.

11

The Good Old Days

'We, too, lived in Arcadia.'
from 'Fifty Years Ago' by Taffy, in *The Broadway*,
March 1955

The Medical School, to which the young Mr Byles's steps would shortly take him, was to remain in use for fifty-three years. It consisted of a basement, a 'ground floor' reached by a flight of steps from the pavement, and first and second floors. The main features were the large lecture theatre, which would accommodate 100 students and was very steeply raked, and the large and extensive museum. The dissecting room was on the upper floor. The chief trouble with the school was that there really were not enough students to make it an economic proposition, for lectures and practical work, in some cases, were provided in no less than twenty-seven different subjects, as is shown in the list of subjects and lectures taken from the school prospectus for the year.

There were, however, many remarkable men

The Medical School in Caxton Street 1885–1938.

93

Mr W. G. Spencer, Surgeon to Westminster 1897–1923.

teaching at that time. Anatomy, for example, was taught by Mr 'Jimmie' Black, a very dynamic man. 'Mr Black, who was aural surgeon to the hospital, was a man of muscle. He usually lectured in his shirt sleeves and as he walked about the room in a state of fervour would sometimes seize the iron rail which separated him from us and shake it with his powerful hands until the pencils jumped off the desks!' (Byles).

The staff on the surgical side was in an interesting state of transformation, for to the senior surgeons, George Cowell, Richard Davy and Nottidge Charles Macnamara, there had been added as assistant surgeons two men who were in their different ways to have the most profound effect on the practice and teaching of surgery in the future. They were Walter G. Spencer and Charles Stonham. George Cowell, Assistant Surgeon 1869–73, Surgeon 1873–96 and who lived until 1921, had performed the first operation in the hospital using the antiseptic methods of Lister. This was ten years previously, in 1877. It was for the removal of an ovarian cyst. It was completely successful, but Lister's methods took a long time to take hold. Richard Davy, that plainspoken man from the West Country would often bring a set of carpenter's tools into the theatre. Byles says, 'in those days when the dangers of sepsis were almost unknown and the surgeon himself was the most septic object in the theatre, a kit of carpenter's tools would not seem out of place'. These were the days when an old frock-coat splashed with blood and pus was kept for operations and never cleaned. It is said that when Dr Richard Hebb was appointed Assistant Physician

Mr Charles Stonham, Assistant-Surgeon to Westminster 1889–96, Surgeon 1896–1916. (Miss Edith Smith)

and Pathologist to the hospital, Davy sent him his operating frock-coat to do duty as a post-mortem garment. Hebb called a porter, picked the awful object off the floor with a pair of tongs and told him to take it away and burn it.

The two new assistant surgeons, Spencer and Stonham were a totally different breed of men.

Dr Richard Hebb, Pathologist 1880–1900 and 1903–18.

WESTMINSTER HOSPITAL MEDICAL SCHOOL

LECTURERS 1887

Clinical Medicine: Dr Sturges, Dr Allchin, Dr Donkin
Clinical Surgery: Mr Cowell, Mr Davy,
  Mr MacNamara
Medicine: Dr Sturges, Dr Allchin, FRSE
Surgery: Mr Cowell, Mr MacNamara
Practical and Operative Surgery: Mr Richard Davy,
  FRSE
Anatomy: Mr Black
Practical Anatomy: Mr Herbert
Physiology, Practical Physiology and Histology:
  Dr Heneage Gibbes
Chemistry: Dr Dupre, FRS and Dr H. Wilson Hake,
  FCS, FIC
Practical Chemistry: Dr H. Wilson Hake
Midwifery and Diseases of Women: Dr Potter
General Pathology and Morbid Anatomy: Dr Allchin,
  FRSE
Morbid Histology: Dr Heneage Gibbes
Materia Medica and Therapeutics: Dr Murrell

Forensic Medicine and Hygiene: Dr de Havilland
  Hall
Toxicology: Dr Dupre, FRS
Psychological Medicine: Dr Sutherland
Ophthalmic Surgery: Mr Cowell
Orthopaedic Surgery: Mr Richard Davy, FRSE
Minor Surgery and Bandaging: Mr Charles Stonham
Diseases of the Skin: Dr Colcott Fox
Aural Surgery: Mr James Black
Dental Surgery: Dr Walker
Laryngoscopy: Dr de Havilland Hall
Botany: Mr H. W. S. Worsley-Benison, FLS
Comparative Anatomy: Dr Leslie Ogilvie
Experimental Physics: Dr George Ogilvie

Treasurer of the School: Mr Cowell
Dean of the School: Dr Donkin
Librarian: Mr John Green

Walter Spencer, 'Pa' Spencer to all who knew him, was a courteous man, very able, and a rapid operator, a master of what is known as 'sharp dissection'. Trained at St Bartholomew's, he came to embody the very spirit of Westminster. He wrote *Westminster Hospital—An Outline of its History*, a book that is open beside the Author at this minute. His old student Dr F. W. W. Dawson said of Mr Spencer—

'He operated in an apron over a mackintosh . . . On one occasion he got an artery spurt on his collar.' 'On his way home, it was in autumn, during the time of Jack the Ripper, as he crossed the Green Park, he was arrested by an observant young policeman and taken to Westminster Police Court. His house surgeon was sent down and managed to persuade them to release him.'

The Good Old Days

Charles Stonham was a totally different man, something of a dandy, with monocle and cavalry moustache. He belonged to that almost vanished breed of surgeons who relieved their nerves while operating by lurid language and throwing things. Yet, when a student of his fell ill with cellulitis following a pricked finger, he showed the essential kindliness and compassion beneath the irascible exterior. He hardly left his side, did all he could for him and was with him when he died. Stonham was famous for two other facets of his career: he was an authority on birds and wrote a book about them, and was the organiser of 'The Imperial Yeomanry Field Hospital and Bearer Company' which saw service in the Boer War 1900–01 and to which reference will be made later.

The physicians of the day were no less remarkable in their way. W. H. Allchin, later Sir William Allchin, K.C.V.O., and Physician Extraordinary to George V was a brilliant teacher, not only of medicine but also of pathology. He was twice Dean of the Medical School in 1878–83 and from 1891–93. Dr de Havilland Hall was a 'tall man with a beard (says his old student 'Hereward') and he taught medicine by rule and line most conscientiously. The correct signs and symptoms, as laid down in textbooks, were emphasised and no other were allowed to exist'. Another student ('Taffy') mentioned his love of mnemonics. 'Being asked by him to state the causes of coma it was sufficient for us to chant in chorus A.E.I.O.U. (A for alcohol, E for epilepsy, I for injury, O for opium or other narcotic poison, U for uraemia or other constitutional disease (diabetes)).' Dr Dawson,

Sir William Allchin, K.C.V.O., Physician to Westminster 1873–1905.

however, who was his House Physician in 1901, tells of a lighter side. 'When he held a bedside class in the ward, the patient was one of alcoholic cirrhosis of the liver. During the proceedings she came out of her semi-coma. Seeing Dr Hall she turned to Sister and said, "A tot of gin, dearie—the gentleman will pay!"'

Sir William Allchin's monaural stethoscope in the possession of Sir Peter Kerley.

97

Sir Horatio Bryan Donkin was the Medical Inspector of Prisons. He was a small, chubby, kindhearted man, always ready to help a sick student. But the man who left his mark on the students was Richard Hebb, physician and pathologist. He was a great sceptic, believed what he himself knew, and had no great opinion of textbook learning. He acted as pathologist from 1880–1900 and was reappointed in 1903–18 following the very serious illness that overtook the first salaried pathologist, W. S. Lazarus-Barlow. He was followed in 1919 by a pupil of his, Dr J. A. Braxton-Hicks (1919–31). Such were the teachers. What about the students in those days? In 1889 the Dean's report (Dr Horatio Bryan Donkin) mentions the successes of the football team! But the list of old students of the day contains an even more striking name, that of W. G. Grace. He had attended ward rounds and out-patients of Dr de Havilland Hall in the years 1878–79 before qualifying L.R.C.P. (Edin.) in 1879. In the 1890 session a Mr A. H. Evans gained an Entrance Scholarship, and in 1891–93 won the Senior Class Prizes in anatomy, physiology and histology. In 1894 he won the prize for pathology, and in 1897–98 the Frederic Bird Medal and Prize. In 1896 E. R. Carling won the Entrance Scholarship and tied for the Treasurer's Prize. Both these men, Mr Arthur Evans and Mr E. Rock Carling (later Sir Ernest Rock Carling) were appointed to the surgical staff. Brilliant pupils of splendid teachers!

In the interim the hospital once again needed attention. The main drainage was finally attended to in 1895, but it necessitated closing the hospital from

The Hospital in 1899.

The dressers to the Imperial Yeomanry Field Company.
From left to right: (*back row*) Mr Crowther, Mr Hughes, Mr Gill; (*front row*) Mr Marrett, Mr Carling, Mr Nimmo.

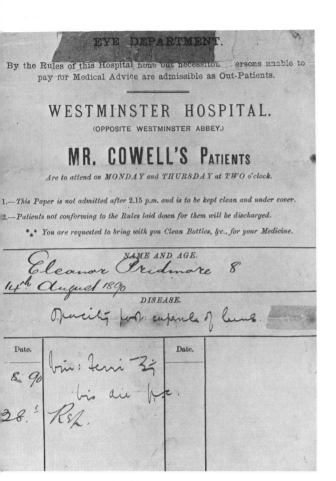

WESTMINSTER HOSPITAL.

(OPPOSITE WESTMINSTER ABBEY.)

MR. COWELL'S PATIENTS

Are to attend on MONDAY and THURSDAY at TWO o'clock.

1.—*This Paper is not admitted after 2.15 p.m. and is to be kept clean and under cover.*

2.—*Patients not conforming to the Rules laid down for them will be discharged.*

** You are requested to bring with you Clean Bottles, &c., for your Medicine.

NAME AND AGE.

Eleanor Pridmore 8
4th August 1890

DISEASE.

Opacity post: capsule of lens

Date.		Date.
8. 90	Vin: ferri ℨj bis die pc.	
28.	R&L	

A patient's 'notes' of 1890.

99

10th July to 22nd October. In 1897 the operating theatre was renovated, and in 1899 the clinical laboratory was built on the west side of the roof. It was opened on 12th July 1900 by Lord Lister, who symbolically subcultured the original Koch strain of tubercle bacillus which had been maintained in the hospital for many years by Dr Hebb. The new laboratory, with its much admired 16-watt electric lighting was one of the first, if not actually the first, hospital laboratory in London constructed specially for performing tests on patients.

But four months before this the 'Imperial Yeomanry Field Hospital and Bearer Company' had left Liverpool Street Station on its way to the Boer War. This body was commanded by Charles Stonham, with the rank of Major (R.A.M.C.). Under him were three civil surgeons, T. H. Openshaw, W. A. Sheen and Mr Arthur Evans, imperiously summoned by telegram by Stonham from Liverpool, where he was then Resident Surgical Officer. There were also present Dr James Purves Stewart, Assistant Physician to Westminster 1898–1912 and Physician 1912–31, who became later one of the world's leading neurologists. He went as physician and anaesthetist! Seven medical students, six from Westminster and one from 'the Hospital at Hyde Park Corner' went as dressers with the honorary rank of private. They were Messrs H. C. Jefferys, S. W. Crowther, C. A. Gill, C. H. M. Hughes, P. J. Marrett, W. C. Nimmo and E. Rock Carling. Their ship, the tramp S.S. *Winkfield*, arrived at Cape Town on 6th April after colliding with and sinking the R.M.S.S. *Mexican* in the fog on 4th April.

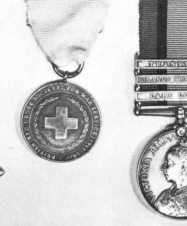

Mr A. H. Evans, O.B.E., Student and Surgeon to Westminster 1891–1936.

Mr A. H. Evans's stethoscope with his O.B.E., International Red Cross Medal, and South African War medal.

Not a very auspicious start to the campaign. Fortunately no lives were lost. In South Africa the Field Hospital marched 1,269 miles: as the wagons were drawn by mules this was a most educational journey. On 7th June the Field Hospital became prisoners of a Boer commando, led by General Christian de Wet, at Roodewal Station, where some 500 men of the Derby militia were surrounded and captured. However, they were rescued by the British forces on 12th June. After many other excitements the party returned to England on 31st March 1901, Mr Evans and all the dressers but two having returned some months previously. For these services Mr Stonham was created Commander of the Order of St Michael and St George. On his return to England Mr Arthur Evans was appointed Assistant Surgeon to the hospital in 1902, becoming Surgeon in 1919. He then began a career in surgery that was amazing in its versatility and skill. There was no field in which he did not excel. His most celebrated case was to remove a cancer of the upper end of the oesophagus in 1909—the first time this had ever been done successfully. The patient was alive and well in the 1930s. If he had a fault it was, perhaps, a total lack of worldly ambition. No man was better loved by his patients and those students fortunate enough to act as his dressers.

100

The Good Old Days

When E. Rock Carling returned to England it was to receive the Gold Medal in the M.B. The late Sister Green ('little Sister Green of Hallett Ward' as she was in the thirties) told how she had, 'dressed Mr Carling's septic finger the day he went up to get his Gold Medal while the bells were tolling for the death of Queen Victoria'. He, too, became Assistant Surgeon to the hospital 1906–23 and Surgeon 1924–42. In the year 1902–03, Dr A. M. Gossage was appointed Dean of the Medical School. He was 'Jimmie' Black's first pupil, the first Westminster man to be made Dean, and the last Westminster man to be appointed Physician to Westminster until 1965. He was Assistant Physician from 1895 to 1912 and Physician 1912 to 1918. Incidentally, only two other Westminster students have been made Dean of the Medical School: E. Rock Carling in 1910–12 and the present Dean, Dr J. B. Wyman, M.B.E., installed in 1964.

A famous teacher in those days was the celebrated Dr Monkton Copeman, F.R.S. He was a world

Dr Monckton Copeman, F.R.S.

THE DEANS OF THE MEDICAL SCHOOL 1912–1964

D. W. Carmalt-Jones	1912–1914
S. A. Kinnier Wilson	1914–1919
Sir Stanley Woodwark, CMG, CBE	1920–1934
Sir Adolphe Abrahams	1934–1940
Mr G. H. Macnab	1940–1950
Mr H. E. Harding	1950–1960
Dr R. I. S. Bayliss	1960–1964
Dr J. B. Wyman, MBE	1964–

authority on vaccination against smallpox and had discovered that glycerin added to raw vaccine lymph killed the bacteria present but left the essential virus unharmed. His students saw him as a crusader, and so pictured him. It is a pleasure to think that his grandson, Dr Peter Copeman, is now on the staff of the Hospital.

Shortly after the turn of the century it was noted that the hospital expenditure was outrunning its income, and in 1905 it was noted that the expenditure was £21,371 and the income only £10,886. There were several interesting occasions which produced

The Sisters at the Ladies Bazaar of 1905.
From left to right: (back row) Sisters King William, Adelaide, Arden, Percy, Hutchinson, Matthew, Fricker; (front row) Sisters Marie Celeste, Night Sisters Webberley, Northumberland, Hollond.

large sums. In 1905 a Ladies Bazaar was held under the direct patronage of Their Majesties, King Edward VII and Queen Alexandra. The affair was sponsored by Her Royal Highness, The Princess of Wales, and six other Royal personages. No less than eleven

Duchesses were on the committee. It brought in £6,618. In 1907 a dinner in the Inner Temple Hall brought in £12,000 and in the same year the Trustees of S. R. Zunz endowed a ward in memory of 'Annie Zunz', this name replacing that of Queen Anne. It may be pointed out that the site of the hospital came in very usefully when money was needed. At Queen Victoria's Coronation the hospital received £3,379, and at her Jubilee £3,370 by the letting of seats to spectators. Similarly, from the Coronation of King Edward VII (1901) the receipts were £7,809, the Coronation of George V yielded over £14,000 and that of George VI £17,838 1s. 3d.

The other important event in 1905 was the decision to stop the teaching of anatomy and physiology and the other pre-clinical subjects at the Medical School, and to concentrate not only Westminster but St George's and Charing Cross students at King's College, London, where they could join the students of King's College Hospital in instruction in these subjects. This decision was regarded as a remarkably sapient one at the time, both the *Lancet* and the *British Medical Journal* being loud in its praise. The University of London was also much in favour. Westminster students have been there (at King's College) for the past sixty years. One of the features of student life at this time was *The Broadway*, a magazine written and published by students, begun in 1899. This organ (officially the *Westminster Hospital Gazette*) has managed to survive to this day (with a sad hibernation from 1915–19). In its pages the student body has preserved a most useful vein of expression

102

The Good Old Days

Wounded soldiers on hospital steps, 1917.

and criticism, paying tribute to the lively minds and exuberant talents of its many devoted editors. In the early numbers many interesting historical facts can be gleaned. Thus, 'Miss Porter the last of the old pre-training school nurses retired in 1902'. Again, *The Broadway* notes the death of the hospital dispenser,

Mr Cobden, in 1900. He was the inventor of the sugar-coated pill and, thus, a real benefactor of humanity. When Mr Gorringe died in 1909 it became known that a very substantial legacy would come to the hospital after the death of Mrs Gorringe. This caused the Medical Committee to revive the plan of removing

103

the nurses sleeping in the hospital to make way for more wards. This triggered off a most elaborate scheme to amalgamate with St George's Hospital either on Clapham Common or on the river near Wandsworth Bridge. The Clapham site was even purchased (on a mortgage) but the negotiations fell through. These ideas were still in the minds of the Governors and staff up to 1919 when a similar association with King's College Hospital also fell through. When the First World War came in 1914 the Governors offered 150 of the beds for military service, and V.A.D. nurses were accepted for training. The Medical School, also, was taken over by the Army for training pathologists, who even worked in the museum, using buckets of water in lieu of proper sinks. By 1915 there was but one student, but it is said that St Thomas's at the same time had only five.

However, there had joined the student body in 1914 a most remarkable man, Stanford Cade. He has told us how, when he went to King's College, he and a fellow student, the late Jack Gorsky, were asked to go for a row on the Thames. They agreed and found themselves rowing Acti 1g Sub-Lieutenant Cecil Wakeley (who later became Sir Cecil Wakeley, P.R.C.S.). It was a strange beginning to such a distinguished career.

The hospital during the war took certain steps which showed that the innate conservatism of the Governors could lend an ear to liberal ideas. In 1916 they decided to admit women medical students, thus finally reversing a decision made in 1861 by the School Council when Miss Elizabeth Garrett applied for admission. Women students were taken up to 1928, but not from 1928 until 1946, when they were once more admitted. Another example of their desire to move with the times arose when the London County Council decided to take active measures to deal with the vast increase in venereal disease which the war had brought in its train. The first of the special clinics to deal with these diseases was set up at the hospital in 1916. This finally ended discussion and policy changes that had been carried on since 1736.

During these dark days the hospital suffered many losses. Charles Stonham took his field hospital to Mesopotamia; he fell gravely ill with malaria and dysentery and returned to London a shattered wreck. He died in 1916. Of him, and those other Westminster men who died in this war, it can only be said, 'But these were men of mercy whose righteous deeds have not been forgotten'.

Then came the Armistice and Peace, and the hospital and the school faced yet once more severe strains and trials.

The Obstetric Department—The Early Years

'Many poor, honest women with child . . . want necessaries
during their lying in . . . the Society proposes to provide
them . . . and with nurses . . . Charitable Proposal.'
Preface to Westminster Hospital Minutes,
Vol. 1, 1715/1716

It is clear from the Minutes that the problems posed
by pregnant women were much on the minds of the
founders of the hospital. Mrs Sherman, the midwife,
saw several pregnant women on behalf of the Charitable Society (Chapter 2). Yet the whole history of
obstetrics in the early days is extremely meagre; there
is no mention of the subject or of obstetric teaching in
the hospital minutes until 1849. It is said that Sir
Charles Leucock, the famous accoucheur who delivered
Queen Victoria's children and, hence, was known as
'The Great Deliverer of His Country' lectured to the
students in the early years of the School. However, in
the Prospectus of the School of Medicine, Session
1849–50, reference is made to the Maternity Charity,
Physicians Dr Frederic Bird and Dr W. Merriman,
Surgeon Mr Greenhalgh. Here it states that this
Charity (The Westminster Hospital Maternity
Charity) affords attendance to 500 lying-in patients
annually and that pupils studying Midwifery under
Dr Frederic Bird will be furnished with cases from the
Maternity Charity under the direction of the Medical
Officers. Dr Bird was a remarkable man. He was born
at Colchester on January 23rd 1818 and received his
medical education at Guy's Hospital. In 1840 he held
the post of clinical assistant at Westminster, being much
influenced by Dr Hamilton Roe, and performed many
operations for the removal of pus from the thorax. He
then took up the dangerous study of ovariotomy (the
operative removal of ovarian tumours or cysts). These
lesions are extremely common and, left untreated, as
they were in the pre-anaesthetic, pre-Listerian days,
grew to enormous size, causing years of misery to the
poor sufferers. The first successful ovariotomy was performed by Ephraim McDowell of Danville, Kentucky.
Dr Bird, then aged 25, performed the first successful
ovariotomy in London. The patient, a Mrs Geesthorpe

aged 35, was operated on in her own house on June 26th 1843 in the presence of Dr Hamilton Roe, Mr B. Phillips, Dr Andrews, Mr Cantis and Mr Brown of Chelsea. The tumour weighed about 20 lb and the operation was entirely satisfactory. A second and third case soon followed and the third patient from whom Bird removed a tumour of 36 lb weight presented him with a fruit dish of French pottery made by the firm of Honoré in Paris, bearing a medallion which states—

Presented
to
Dr Frederic Bird

by Mrs Williams of Park Terrace R.P. [Regents Park-Ed.] in grateful acknowledgement for the vast skill and tender care he evinced in removing a large ovarian tumour weighing 36 lbs on the 28th of Jan. 1844 by which she has been saved from an early grave.

A grateful patient, indeed! In all, Dr Bird operated on thirteen cases, nine of which were successful. However, he found the strain of such operations was too great and he gave up performing them. He was appointed Obstetric Physician to Westminster Hospital in 1861 and continued as a Lecturer at the School 'eloquent, terse, yet happy mode of expression' until his untimely death in 1874. His widow left a sum of money to provide the Frederic Bird Prize and Medal. Three years after he was put on the staff, Arden ward was opened for obstetric cases.

Dr Bird was succeeded by his friend and colleague

Dr Frederic Bird, Lecturer in Midwifery 1840–74. Obstetric Physician 1861–74. (Rex Roberts Studios, Dublin)

The Obstetric Department

Enamelled fruit bowl presented to Dr Frederic Bird by a grateful patient. (Rex Roberts Studios, Dublin)

Dr John Baptiste Potter who had joined him as Assistant Obstetric Physician in 1870. Dr Potter was renowned for the luxuriance of his beard and the amazing dexterity of his fingers. He assisted Mr George Cowell in his successful ovariotomy, using Lister's antiseptic method in 1877. Dr Potter retired in 1900. It is certain that no wards were set apart for gynaecological cases until 1924, such cases as required admission being usually admitted under surgeons into

surgical wards! The post of Resident Obstetric Assistant was introduced as long ago as 1871. It was held in 1895 by Mr A. H. Evans who recalled (says Briant Evans) having to fetch Dr Potter in a hansom cab to attend severe emergencies. There was evidently plenty of work, for Dr William Chapman Gregg was put on the staff as Assistant Obstetric Physician from 1874 to 1893. He was followed in this post by Dr W. Rivers Pollock from 1893 to 1900, when he succeeded Dr Potter in the senior post, which he held until 1909. Rivers Pollock had been an athlete in his youth and had thrombosed his inferior vena cava following a hurdle race when a young man at the Oxford and Cambridge University Athletic match. Following this unfortunate event he was forced to wear a number of elastic bandages to assist the return of blood from the lower part of the body to the heart. Despite this gross handicap he carried out his duties and his obstetric practice without complaint of any kind until his death. He was a very brave and most talented man.

In 1901, G. Drummond Robinson was elected as the last Assistant Obstetric Physician, becoming full Obstetric Physician in 1909, a post he held until 1924. In 1909, Stanley Dodd was elected Assistant Obstetric Surgeon; he was an old Westminster student and had gained an Entrance Scholarship in 1894. He held the post of House Surgeon in 1902 and House Physician in 1903. In 1924 he became Full Surgeon, a post he held until 1936. In 1924, Aubrey Goodwin became Assistant until 1936. Mr Goodwin (*see* Chapter 14) retired in 1954. In the thirties there was a succession of most outstanding Obstetric Registrars, the late Sir

THE OBSTETRIC DEPARTMENT

Obstetric Physicians

Frederic Bird	1861–1874
John Baptiste Potter (Asst Physn 1870–1874)	1874–1900
William Chapman Gregg (Asst Physn 1874–1893)	
W. Rivers Pollock (Asst Physn 1893–1900)	1901–1909
G. Drummond Robinson (Asst Physn 1901–1909)	1909–1924

Obstetric Surgeons

Stanley Dodd (Asst Surg 1909–1924)	1924–1936
Aubrey Goodwin, OBE (Asst Surgn 1924–1936)	1936–1954
Sir Arthur Bell (Asst Surgn 1936–1954)	1954–1970
W. N. Searle (Asst Surgn 1939–1954)	
A. Briant Evans	1948–1972
R. de Vere	1954–

Professorial Obstetric Department

Professor P. Curzen	1970–
Senior Lecturer: W. L. Whitehouse	1964–

The Coles Quads aged 6.

Charles Read, Sir Arthur Bell, the late Walter Netley Searle and Mr A. Briant Evans. The last three of these, of course, were all elected to the staff. Mr Searle had one particular distinction—he delivered the 'Coles' quadruplets, the first quadruplets ever successfully delivered in a Teaching Hospital. This was in 1950.

It was in this way that the Obstetric Department began its distinguished career and reached its present position of such high distinction.

At the present time much interest is being taken in

108

The Obstetric Department

the phenomenon of childbirth as is shown by the presentation of films on television of children being born. Westminster has a pioneer in this field. Drummond-Robinson in 1917–18 arranged for films of both normal and breech deliveries to be made. Mr Bowdler Henry, who actually delivered the babies, vividly recalls the heat of the carbon-arc lamps. The photographer was a free-lance professional. The film was 'screened' on the Bioscope at the Palace Theatre for the students and was also shown at the Obstetric Section of the Royal Society of Medicine on 6th November 1919, where it created much discussion.

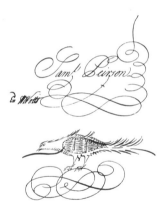

13

Sunset in the Sanctuary, 1919–1939

'So that the Hospital can move.'

Evening News, 1st November 1933

The problems facing the Governors and the staff in 1919 were numerous and alarming. The hospital building was dilapidated and the improvements suggested in 1910 had not been carried out. The financial position was precarious because of the late war, and the hospital was without certain special departments—Ear, Nose and Throat, Ophthalmology and similar special subjects—which caused the University of London to view it with suspicion as a teaching hospital. It is for this reason that the proposed amalgamation with King's College Hospital, mentioned in the last chapter, arose. Again, the staff was much depleted and the problem of the Medical School re-opening with so few students (it is said that there were but four students in 1919) remained to be solved.

Following the death of Sir Rutherford Alcock, in 1897, the post of Chairman of the House Committee had been taken by Sir John Wolfe Barry, who served until 1918. Lord Glenconner thus was faced with these problems from 1918 to 1920, and he was followed in office by Sir Edward Pearson (1921–26). To his committee was submitted a memorandum by the staff. They included only those things that *could* be done in the old building: repainting and cleansing the whole hospital, the introduction of a hot-water system, another operating theatre, nursing accommodation and better quarters for the resident staff. Their most powerful argument was the following: 'Until beds are provided for the treatment of eye, ear, nose and throat diseases and midwifery, candidates for M.S. and M.D. degrees must go elsewhere for their instruction. The Medical Staff, unwilling that the Hospital and School should sink into a secondary position, feels that this is a matter of real urgency.'

The Governors, stimulated by Sir Edward Pearson, reacted vigorously. The money was raised, some £70,000, and on 1st July 1923 the hospital was 'closed for improvements'. The students went to Charing Cross, the out-patients to the Medical School. In *The*

Nursing Staff 1922.

Broadway of October 1923, the Editor, M.N.O., printed the following adaptation of Wordsworth:

'The eighth great wonder of the world is there!
Dull would he be of mind who could pass by
A sight so drear, which yet hath majesty.
This edifice doth like a garment wear
The scaffoldings of repair; silent, bare
Bricks, mortar, slates, supplies and waggons lie
Open to the square and to the sky,
All drab and lowering in the smokeless air.
Never more mockingly did Phoebus steep
In his first splendour, Broadway, road or street.
Ne'er saw I, never felt a calm so deep
The students saunter at their own sweet will
Quoth they "The very workmen seem asleep"
Whilst all our mighty work is lying still.'

The same issue notes with feeling, 'It takes fifteen men to make a Rugby team, though we now have seven times as many students as at the end of the war, we have not yet enough to run a regular team.'

On 15th July 1924 a Solemn Service of Thanksgiving was held in the Abbey. The congregation included the medical staff, the house committee, the treasurers, the Mayor and Corporation of Westminster, the administrative staff, the resident medical officers, the nurses, the students and a new body, the massage students! A School of Massage had been started in 1919, the new students accommodated in the basement of the Medical School, and carefully segregated, of course, from the medical students prowling above them.

The hospital was re-opened in 1st August 1924. The President, H.R.H. The Prince of Wales toured

Sir Stanley Woodwark, C.M.G., C.B.E., Dean of the Medical School 1920–34, Physician to Westminster 1919–40.

the wards on 11th November and was greeted by the students with great and affectionate enthusiasm. Once more the hospital took on its proper function as a Teaching Hospital, this time complete with the special departments it had previously lacked. The medical staff threw into their work such energy and devotion that the school rapidly grew in numbers and enthusiasm. This process was aided by the Dean, Sir Stanley Woodwark, who persuaded the Medical School Council to offer scholarships to be held during the clinical period of instruction to students nominated by the headmasters of their schools. Sir Stanley was a tall, genial man, handsome and a witty speaker. His textbook of medicine ran into several editions. He is well remembered by his ingenious mnemonics, a favourite story about him being, 'Wednesday for Women, said Sir Stanley Woodwark turning into King William (the men's ward)'. As a man he was very kind to his students and to his House Physician.

A particular student of those days was, of course, the late C. P. Thomas who became in later life Sir Clement Price Thomas K.C.V.O. He had begun his professional career as a dental student at Cardiff, and joined a field ambulance during the First World War. This had induced in him a deep loathing of mules and a great desire to be a surgeon. Coming to Westminster in 1919 he came under the spell of Tudor Edwards, and like him, was first attracted to urology as a speciality before being irresistibly drawn in his footsteps to become a chest surgeon. It is a fortunate coincidence that I. W. Magill, now Sir Ivan Magill, K.C.V.O., the great pioneer of endotracheal anaesthesia, joined the staff at this time. The advances of surgery were thus matched with the necessary advances in anaesthetic technique, a dual partnership which continued harmoniously for many years.

One other surgeon must be mentioned at this point

The Hospital in the 1930s after the renovations of 1923–4.

of time for his influence on students and fellow members of the staff; it was quite remarkable. This is G. T. Mullally—so many of us are in his debt, both for his influence as a teacher and as a source of inspiration, that I need say no more about this truly great man. In the late twenties, Stanford Cade (now Sir Stanford Cade, K.B.E., C.B.) backed by Sir Ernest Rock Carling and inspired by his old chief, Walter G. Spencer, began the development of radiation therapy by large masses of radium. The earlier units, indeed, were designed by Mr Carling, son of Sir Ernest. The potential use of this type of therapy was so great that soon a 'Radium Annexe' was built.

It was opened by Viscount Lee of Fareham, P.C. in 1930. It was unfortunately as far away as Fitzjohn's Avenue, Hampstead. The radium for the first 'bombs' was bought from the Belgian Congo by the Government and the first single gramme cost £14,000. The Annexe contained 22 beds only, but while the clinical applications of the new methods were being studied Professor Flint and Dr Grimmett began those long series of precise measurements of dose intensity that were later brought to such a pitch of perfection by Dr C. Wilson, the late physicist to the hospital. In this way the new method of treatment, being precisely understood, became safe for the patient undergoing it.

113

Sir James Purves-Stewart's last round. Behind Sir James is Sir Adolphe Abrahams. Left foreground: *Dr G. S. W. Organe.* (Fox Photos)

During this period the physicians, too, were not in any way static. Sir James Purves Stewart's demonstrations of neurology drew visitors from all over the world. He possessed that curious trick, almost of showmanship, found in many great teachers, which employs a slight exaggeration of a normal gesture to ram home a point. To see him take the patient's pulse or elucidate the Babinski reflexes, left no doubt in the audience's mind of the essential importance of these fundamental acts. His retinue, too, was impressive: the House Physician carried his gold patella hammer; his secretary attended to take notes and his chauffeur carried a bag containing his other instruments. When

he entered the ward followed by these functionaries, the Sister and her nurses and the students and visitors, the patients could not fail to be impressed. Towards the end of his career as a physician to the hospital Sir James began an investigation into the cause and treatment of multiple sclerosis, and a research worker was employed to carry out the laboratory side of the work. Cerebrospinal fluid was taken from the patients and cultured in a special medium. When this was examined by a microscopic technique called 'dark ground illumination', tiny shining dots could be seen against a black background. The mixture was diluted to a standard number of particles and employed as a vaccine. It was claimed that these particles were the causative agent of the disease and they were called 'insula spherularis'. The results were published and

Dr Braxton Hicks, Student 1902, Pathologist to Westminster 1919–30.

114

R. J. V. Pulvertaft, Professor of Clinical Pathology, London University: Pathologist to Westminster 1930–62.

Pulvertaft was appointed Pathologist. He was educated at Westminster School and had been in the Air Force in the war as a bomber pilot—indeed, it is said that for many years afterwards he never slowed down at corners when driving a car in case it stalled and then crashed! A measure of his success as a teacher, by no means orthodox, lies in the fact that there are in London University alone no less than four Professors and one Reader of Pathology or Bacteriology who had been students under him.

Before proceeding with events in strict chronological order, two appointments had been made early in this period of personalities, so powerful that it is impossible to imagine the hospital without their presence and inspiration. The first was that of Miss Edith Smith, O.B.E., R.R.C., as Matron, which took place in 1915

the preparations were demonstrated at a scientific meeting. A visiting savant pointed out that the 'insula spherularis' was, in fact, merely a form of the minute organisms called today mycoplasma, then known to cause bovine pleuro-pneumonia. The result of this bombshell was, of course, decisive. The research worker resigned and the Director of the Laboratories, Dr Braxton Hicks, although he was not in any way responsible for this research, felt in honour bound to resign also. It was an episode that left little credit to those most deeply involved. Following the resignation of Dr Braxton Hicks, Dr (now Professor) R. J. V.

115

Miss Edith Smith, O.B.E., R.R.C., Matron Westminster Hospital 1915–48.

following the retirement of Miss E. S. Young to become Mrs Vaux Graham, happily still hale and hearty in 1966 at the age of 94! Miss Smith is one of the great matrons of all times—her striking personality raised the standard of Westminster nursing to a level that made all other nursing schools jealous, and no higher praise could be given than that.

The other appointment was Mr Charles M. Power, O.B.E., M.C., as Hospital Secretary. He was the third to be elected since 1832, for the first, Mr F. J. Wilson, served until 1878 and was followed by Mr S. M. Quennell, who retired in 1921. Mr Power was to serve until his death (much lamented) in 1954. His integrity and driving force were shortly to be tested to the uttermost, both in the negotiations and planning of the present hospital, and in the difficult times of the Second World War. It had been quite apparent to those who looked ahead in 1924 that it would be impossible to expand the hospital, nurses' home and Medical School on their present sites and that sooner or later this decision must be faced. The hour struck in 1933, a site totalling some 66,000 square feet on both sides of St John's Gardens had become available. To secure an option on it, £100,000 had to be raised or guaranteed by 31st March 1934 and a further £250,000 would be needed to begin building on the site. The House Committee rose to the challenge. The Chairman, K. A. Wolfe Barry, O.B.E. and the two Treasurers, Edward H. Hoare and F. C. Goodenough were backed up by a strong medical representation. They were Mr Spencer, Dr Thompson Barron, Mr E. Rock Carling, Mr Gilbert Chubb, Dr de Souza, Mr

Sir Ernest Rock Carling, Student and Surgeon to Westminster 1896–1960.

Arthur Evans, Mr G. T. Mullally, Mr William Turner, Mr A. F. MacCallan, Dr Arnold Stott and Dr Stanley Woodwark. Even though in 1935 the committee lost its Chairman, his place was filled by another, Sir Bernard Docker, whose labours on behalf of the hospital rival (says Langdon Davies) Sir Rutherford Alcock himself. The actual planning of the hospital, school and nurses' home were entrusted to an Executive Planning Committee, which consisted of Sir Bernard Docker (the Chairman), Mr Power, Mr Maurice Webb, architect and member of the Board of Governors, another Governor, J. D. C. Couper, a consulting engineer, and Mr Rock Carling. To design this new undertaking account had to be taken of the University and its requirements, the Ministry of Health, the London County Council and the size of the hospital endowments. Furthermore, the varying needs of the different specialists on the hospital staff had to be taken into account, and where possible, the changes of a distant future could not be ignored. It was here that Mr Carling came into his own. His great integrity and love of the hospital gave him the confidence of his colleagues. He, with Mr Stanford Cade, Dr Peter Kerley and Mr Power travelled widely on the Continent and in America, and the end-product is the hospital, school and nurses' home of today. The man who put all their ideas into solid and enduring form was the architect, Mr Lionel Pearson. He was much ahead of his time and the concepts to which he gave the cladding were quite revolutionary for those days. On 26th June 1935, the President, H.R.H. the Prince of Wales, laid the foundation stone of the nurses' home and this, the first part of the new building scheme, was declared open in March 1938 by H. M. Queen Mary, who gave her gracious permission for it to be called the 'Queen Mary Nurses' Home'. The Medical School was opened later in 1938 by the Earl of Athlone.

Finally, on 20th April 1939 the hospital was declared open by H.M. George VI, Patron to the hospital, accompanied by H.M. Queen Elizabeth. It was a great day for Westminster! But before this happy rebirth of the hospital changes had taken place in the staff, of whom it is fitting to mention the outstanding members in the 1930s. Mr William Turner, who had been Lord Lister's last House Surgeon at King's, had joined the staff as Assistant Surgeon in 1897. In 1916 he became Surgeon, and retired in 1934. Mr Arthur Evans retired in 1936. The Author remembers a remarkable event, in 1936, which took place in the post-mortem room on the roof of the old hospital. A specimen from a patient who had for many years been under the care of the hospital was being demonstrated. There was no other student but Mr Walter Spencer, red-faced, bluff-countenanced with a wing collar and a pearl tie-pin, was there. Next to him stood Mr Turner in a neat black suit, his left lower lip caught between his teeth muttering something about its being a 'very tricky case'. Next to him was Mr Evans, white-haired, a little stooped, talking in his high clear voice, his eyeglasses in his hand with their broad, black, silk ribbon round his neck. Next to him Mr Carling in his rimless glasses, a little aloof, precise in his diction, and next to him, G. T. Mullally, hands in pockets, nodding gently and saying, 'Yes, yes, yes'. All these men had attended the patient in their time and all had been, or would be, Senior Surgeon to the Hospital! The physicians too, in their way, were equally remarkable. Dr de Souza was a small man, very learned in his profession who, when he retired took up Law and was made a Barrister. Unfortunately,

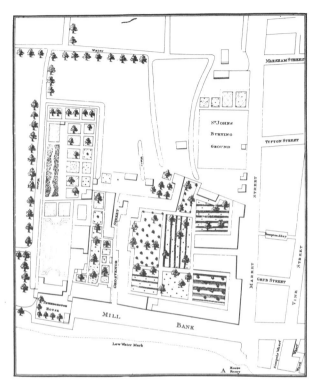

Westminster Hospital 1716–1974

The Medical School and Hospital Site.
Left, 1740. Below, 1936.
Opposite: The Hospital and Medical School today.

Opening of the new Medical School by the Rt. Hon. The Earl of Athlone, Chancellor of London University 1938 (Photopress)

he spoke so quietly that his teaching rounds were quite painful to attend because of the strain of concentrating for so long. Sir Arnold Stott, as he became, had even in those days a love of precision and good manners and a biting vein of sarcasm if they were in any way infringed. Sir Adolphe Abrahams spent the greater part of his career as physician in the Out-patient Department, then below stairs, where the patients were ruled with a rod of iron by the Senior Porter, 'Tom', Tom Goldsmith, and where the notes were kept under the watchful eye of Miss Gutteridge. Woe betide the person, staff or student, who mislaid them. Sir Adolphe held his Medical Out-patients next door to Mr Mullally's Surgical Out-patients. The friendship between these two men was very real and they would frequently ask each other's opinion, with a little due ceremony, about difficult cases. It was a very difficult case indeed that their combined erudition and experience could not throw light on. However, the star turn for eccentricity at this time was

120

undoubtedly Hildred Carlill. He was much attracted to that branch of medicine where neurology and psychiatry become irretrievably intermingled. His patients, therefore, tended to have strange histories and even stranger behaviour. Hildred Carlill's approach was one of utter but devastating thoroughness. Every aspect of their life and habit was inquired into with the most intimate questions asked in a very loud voice. His cry, 'Speak up, we're all doctors here' was often heard. The patients, too, would be examined in the greatest detail and would often find themselves parading down the ward stark naked, keenly pursued by Dr C. and his clerks. He had another foible, namely, that many obscure ills could be cured by removing the appendix, and he badgered many of the staff to perform these operations for him. None the less, he was a very good doctor and, of course, as one might expect, an accomplished hypnoteur. He never failed to warn students of the dangers of hypnosis and never used it until all other measures failed.

The special departments too, had their virtuosos. In the Ophthalmic Department the kindly and dexterous Mr Griffith was partnered by Mr A. F. MacCallan. This gentleman had become the world authority on that devastating disease, trachoma, and his work in Egypt on this and other subjects had earned him the special thanks of the Egyptian Government, who put up a bust to him, and of the British Government, who created him a Commander of the Order of the British Empire. He tended to become a little nervous before operating and was heard to say to his House Surgeon on one occasion, 'Aaah, (he prefixed most of his sentences with this interjection), you have a cold, you are septic and since it is impracticable to boil you— aah, GET OUT.' Yet he was basically a kindly man and many students enjoyed his hospitality and the many sets of tennis played with him. The Children's Department, also, was noted for Dr Donald Paterson with his lavender waistcoat and his intuitive diagnostic flair. Many people have had cause to be grateful for his elegant and simple methods of baby feeding. One can still hear the basic formula, '$2\frac{1}{2}$ ounces per pound body weight per day' ringing round the old Marie Celeste Ward with its walls tiled with nursery-rhyme stories, where the children took their after-lunch naps to the music of a most beautiful music box. Lunch there, by the way, was always mince and vegetables followed by rice pudding and fresh fruit salad, and very good too. When Dr Paterson felt that the 'firm' were even more obtuse than usual he was wont to sniff devastatingly and utter the clarion call 'Come along you fellows, it's like carrying round a whole load of grand pianos'. In the late thirties medical men from Germany and Austria, dispossessed by Hitler, began to appear as students, studying for an English (or more commonly, a Scottish) degree permitting them to practice in this country. One day Dr Paterson came in full of a paper he had just read in the *Lancet* or the *British Medical Journal*. He catechised the firm thus: 'You—there—have you read it?' 'No sir.' 'You next to him, have you read it?' and so right through the firm. All were ignorant. Finally, he turned to one of these ex-patriated gentlemen and asked him if he had read it. 'Me—I *write* him', was the reply.

The present Hospital 1965. Inset: Sectional diagram.

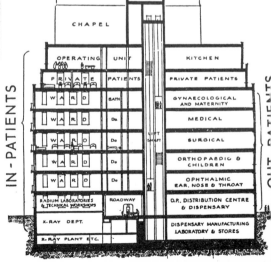

IN-PATIENTS

OUT-PATIENTS

CHAPEL		
OPERATING UNIT		KITCHEN
P R I V A T E PATIENTS		PRIVATE PATIENTS
W A R D	BATH	GYNAECOLOGICAL AND MATERNITY
W A R D	Do	MEDICAL
W A R D	Do	SURGICAL
W A R D	Do	ORTHOPAEDIC & CHILDREN
W A R D	Do	OPHTHALMIC EAR, NOSE & THROAT
RADIUM LABORATORIES & TECHNICAL WORKSHOPS	ROADWAY	O.P. DISTRIBUTION CENTRE & DISPENSARY
X-RAY DEPT.		DISPENSARY MANUFACTURING LABORATORY & STORES
X-RAY PLANT ETC.		

Sunset in the Sanctuary, 1919–1939

As the years from 1935 to 1939 passed there was always at the back of it all the German menace and, indeed, in 1938 this became real in our minds even before Mr Chamberlain had made his famous flight. One member of the staff was even heard to remark, 'I may not be a very good doctor but I am an expert with a machine gun'. But this crisis passed also and, as has been previously stated, the day came when the new hospital was formally opened. The ceremony was held on the vacant Page Street site, covered for the occasion by a huge marquee. Many of those present had seen Their Majesties at their Coronation from the unparalleled vantage point of the old hospital and had seen the sunlight strike red shafts of fire from the Black Prince's ruby in the Imperial State crown when the King and Queen stood at the top of the shallow flight of steps on leaving the Abbey, a transcendent moment. In his speech the King said, 'The new buildings embody a great ideal. The benefactors, whose generosity has made this achievement possible . . . must indeed be gratified today . . . . I congratulate them heartily. . . .' Their Majesties toured the building, and it was a special source of pride that the new children's wards, as yet unnamed, were to bear the names 'Princess Elizabeth' and 'Princess Margaret Rose'. The move from the old to the new buildings was most carefully planned under the direction of Mr Frank Wray—it took place smoothly from 6th to 26th June. On the last night very few patients were left in the old building and all the staff present did a little souvenir hunting. Someone even removed the brass knocker from Matron's bedroom door! As a last

123

The Medical School and Nurses' Home 1965.

gesture a human pyramid was formed and the old gas jets in the ground-floor corridor were lit, the first time for fifty years. Then the old building was left for ever, to its memories and its ghosts. The nun who sat by the dying in Hollond, the soldier's footsteps outside Arden Ward on the duck-boards on the roof, even the visitant who silently unlatched the doors of Marie Celeste at midnight to let a cold draught steal in—they, too, were at last alone with their memories.

In the new hospital there was much to learn and new traditions to set. In the old 'Path. Lab' tea was served to the staff and students in their white coats. To this day, the laboratory staff take tea in the refectory in their white coats. There was much to learn and little time to learn it, for on 3rd September 1939,

The Westminster Fair of 1935.

war was declared and a new challenge to be met.

Throughout the whole of this period many expedients were employed to raise funds for the hospital. Once a year, for example, there was the Hospital Flag Day. On this day bands of students roamed the streets with barrel organs, often in fancy dress. They infested Waterloo and Victoria Stations particularly, as the event was usually held on Derby Day. The flags bore the emblem of a black cat with white markings, the prototype of which was Matron's cat, the descendant of a long line of mousers, probably stroked by Mr Guthrie himself. From time to time more elaborate 'stunts' were devised. In 1924 the students 'kidnapped' (under the willing auspices of the *Daily Mirror*) the famous cartoon characters, Pip, Squeak and Wilfred, and held them to ransom.

In 1935 another Fair was held in Dean's Yard for a week. The event was under the direction of the President of the Hospital, H.R.H. the Prince of Wales, and every day one or other members of the Royal Family attended. One day, Matron drew a shy gentleman on to the dais and announced that Mr Edward Meyerstein, as he then was, had given us £10,000 for the Medical School! A painting of a day at this Fair formerly hung in the Nurses' Home. In 1937, Mr Walt Disney gave the hospital permission to use the famous figures of Micky and Minnie Mouse as fund raisers. He was over here at the time and filmed the resident staff on the hospital steps. Some months later they were the crowd in 'Micky the Giant Killer'. The old hospital held its secrets to the end. When it was finally demolished in 1950 a complete skeleton was found under the foundations at the northern end. Examination showed it to be an anatomist's articulated specimen. Which student introduced it into the foundations is not known. Was it in 1889 or 1834? No one will ever know!

14
The Hospital at War, 1939–1945

'Macnab did a fine job directing the place.'
from a letter from an American doctor to the
Minister of Health, in 1941

Unlike the situation in 1914, there had been thought 'taken for the morrow' in 1939. The Government, fearing a wholesale bomber offensive against London, had prepared most detailed plans for evacuation and the medical services had been especially planned as part of this organisation. London was divided into a series of Sectors as they were called, each containing at least one Teaching Hospital, and certain hospitals on the periphery were attached to them. The south-west sector included Westminster and St George's Hospitals. It extended to include Windsor, Staines, Slough and Twickenham. These plans were largely made by an old Westminster man in the Ministry of Health, the late Sir John Hebb, to whom all credit is due. Two days before war was declared, parties of Sisters and nurses left for their sector posts: thus, Sisters Walters, Mitchell, Hannaford, Williams and Hunt found themselves at the South Middlesex Fever Hospital; Sisters Pearce and Gillette went to Park

Prewett Hospital and Sister James found herself at Old Windsor. The greater part of the laboratory staff went to Staines where Dr (now Professor) Maclagan was to stay, while Dr (now Professor) Pulvertaft joined a unit of the Medical Research Council study-ing air infection, before joining the Army and going to the Middle East. The medical staff had been enrolled in an organisation called the E.M.S. (Emergency Medical Service) and some members went as far away as Newmarket! It was decided to evacuate the operat-ing theatres from the seventh floor to the dental and eye theatres on the first floor. The huge anti-gas curtains over the North and South gates were brought partially our of their slots (they, in the event, made excellent blackout blinds) and other measures were taken. Thus, when the siren went at 11.30 a.m. on 3rd September everybody knew his post and went to it. That nothing happened was an inglorious anti-climax!

The Hospital dressed for War, 1939.

The students, too, had been dispersed widely, at first to Glasgow and later to Birmingham. Of the other hospital departments the obstetric and gynaecology departments remained out of London for the whole of the war. The obstetric cases were housed at Ripley Court and the vast majority of gynaecological cases were accommodated at the South Middlesex Hospital.

In January 1941, at the instigation of the Dean, Mr Macnab, a students' hostel, The Croft, was opened. This was at Stanwell Moor, 'an intriguing Jacobean residence and an attractive old-world garden with lovely old lawns, kitchen garden, orchard and paddock'. The weird tales of the things that happened there are quite incredible, but those who were fortunate enough to be inmates will remember them. The Croft was run by Miss Jean Whalley (now Mrs James

Earle). No one could have done this difficult task more efficiently; the Medical School for ever owes her a deep debt of gratitude. The 'Croft' students attended Ashford County Hospital.

The hospital was put under the care of a Medical Superintendent; for the first year, Mr G. T. Mullally filled this office and he was followed by Mr G. H. Macnab, who remained in charge for the whole of the war. With the private wards empty and most of the hospital also evacuated, the private rooms were allotted to the resident consultant staff. It was a pleasant sight to see them sitting on the balcony each morning reading *The Times* and getting a well-earned rest! Meanwhile, a team of stretcher-bearers was being organised by the Assistant Dental Surgeon to the hospital, Mr G. M. Hickley. As he was Navy trained

Cartoon by N.I.B. of contemporaries at 'The Croft', Staines.
Left to right: Gervaise Woodsend, Tony Fairrie, John Llewellyn-Jones, John Dean, Bill Kennard, John Scrivener.
Below: 'Hoppy' Roberts, Robert Dickson.

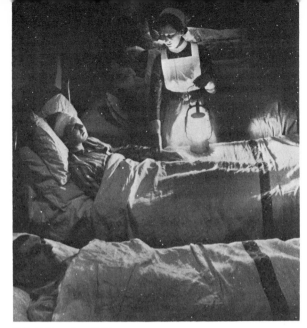

'*Night Round*'—1940.

there were, naturally, port and starboard watches. The bearers themselves came largely from nearby businesses and were so well trained and organised that they were invaluable when their time came. Soon, however, it was apparent that the 'phony war' was on and gradually over the months more beds, even private ones, were opened and many strange patients were seen in them. There were, of course, many sick soldiers: one day thirty huge Guardsmen with influenza arrived in ambulances followed by the illest man of the lot, who marched up complete with full pack and rifle, having missed his transport! A special

dispensation had to be obtained for them to 'lie to attention' instead of leaping out of bed every time a doctor entered the ward. Later, there were Free Poles, Norwegians and French soldiers and, as Sir Stanford had joined the R.A.F., innumerable members of this service also. After a few weeks of war a limited number of students returned and the Dean, Sir Adolphe Abrahams, organised courses of lectures for them so that even during the worst part of the war there was a medical school in being with full and proper courses of instruction. The blackout brought two of the present students' most pleasant occasions into being. These are the Pantomime and the Shrove Tuesday Dinner. The guiding spirit and inspiration was the then Hospital Chaplain, the Reverend Christopher Hildyard, now Sacrist to the Abbey. When Shrove Tuesday, 1940, came round it occurred to 'Chris' that it would make a pleasant evening to have a dinner in the refectory and to have as Guest of Honour, Sir Stanley Woodwark. Sir Stanley entered into the spirit of the occasion—in the middle of a very witty speech he broke off to say that he had finally perfected a cure for sciatica and begged leave to show his first successful case. On receiving consent there then entered a man who walked briskly round the refectory on his hands! However, while this was going on Ian Bartholomew ('Nib' for short) was busily caricaturing Sir Stanley on the tablecloth—all present signed it, and it was cut out and framed, thus starting a most happy tradition, although the present caricatures are now drawn on card before being presented and signed at the dinner.

The Pantomimes began in a small way in 1940 with

Bomb damage in the Chapel 12th November 1940.

Westminster Hospital 1716–1974

nated, and the position had hardly been rectified when on 8th September 1940, a beautiful day, one heard gunfire for the first time and saw a large formation of German bombers flying over London. Shortly after, huge brown clouds of smoke were seen rising from the area of the Docks. That night, as dusk fell, from the north end of the hospital roof Tower Bridge could be seen black against the fires of the burning docks, its bascules raised—a raised drawbridge to a city shortly to be so heavily beseiged. That night the 'vroum-vroum' of German bombers was heard for the first time and the giant stride of a stick of bombs straddling the hospital, a sound, alas, to become very frequent in the months to come. Soon there were ambulances and patients. The Author had the honour of admitting the first. In all, some 600 were admitted between September 1940 and the end of May 1941 with as many more slightly wounded treated as out-patients. No tribute of mine can be great enough for the ambulance drivers, the Heavy Duty Rescue Squads and the firemen who brought them to the hospital, and to the proud and dignified bearing of these victims of a tyrannous assault. It was observed that because the hospital was built on a 'raft' of concrete a near-miss would cause it to waggle like a supple rod—a most curious feeling. The first near-miss landed on a garage built on the far corner of the Page Street site. Later, on a relatively quiet night, 11th September 1940, a tremendous crash shook the hospital and the air-conditioning brought dust and smoke to the nostrils. It took quite a considerable time to discover that an armour-piercing bomb had struck the chapel on the

a short *Cinderella* written by Norman Ashton, followed next year by a most successful *Aladdin*, which Ashton later produced in Africa with an enormous cast. Once the German offensives began in 1940, however, it was apparent that sooner or later the storm would break. When, after Dunkirk, a convoy of wounded was received in the hospital it became apparent that it could not long be delayed. At the beginning of September many members of the staff (in the junior ranks) had their appointments in the E.M.S. termi-

The Hospital at War, 1939–1945

Head of bomb which damaged the Chapel 11th November 1940.

Unexploded aerial land-mine, Greycoat's School 1940. (Mrs M. Mackenzie)

Bomb damage: Annie Zunz Ward 16th November 1940.

north-east corner, high up. It had been fortunately broken in two by a girder and thus deflected. The head was found in a local builder's yard. The chapel was severely damaged but no one was injured. Later in November, on the 21st, during a severe raid another bomb struck the fabric on the north-east corner on the sixth floor; it was again deflected by a girder but the shock brought the ceilings down even in Annie Zunz on the fourth floor. Furthermore, the explosion caused considerable flooding as a tap from the water tanks in the roof was jarred open. A most unusual incident occurred on 7th November 1940 in daylight when a fighter bomber flew down Horseferry Road during the performance of an autopsy. It was firing machine guns and dropped a bomb which hit the traffic island

129

at the foot of Lambeth Bridge. The onlookers at the autopsy took refuge under the table! As the plane passed, a Bofors gun, mounted on top of the I.C.I. building, fired six shots and brought it down. It was an unnerving episode. The bomb did not explode and, later, was seen in the back of a lorry, nonchalantly jammed against the side by a member of the Bomb Disposal Unit taking it away for destruction elsewhere.

The worst episode, however, occurred in the extremely heavy raid of 16th April 1941. A student (now Rear-Admiral) A. O'Connor at the South Gate heard a strange noise and ran to tell Mr Power at the Report Centre in the main hall. He said, 'There's a . . . ' when an enormous explosion occurred. It was a huge parachute-mine which landed in the porch of Cleland House across the road from the South Gate. The blast of this explosion took practically every window from the hospital, nurses' home and medical school on the Garden's side. It was possible to see through the nurses' home to the light of fires burning beyond it. The Author, in Wolfe Barry Ward got the impression that the cone of fire from the bomb actually touched the hospital. The blast tore the iron window frames in the ward on the Page Street side and projected them through the windows on the Garden's side. The cubicle walls on the first, third, fourth and fifth floors collapsed and the private ward lift doors on each floor were buckled. Yet despite all this, by the mercy of God, no one was killed or seriously wounded. Indeed, the only casualties were a stretcher-bearer who had a pair of doors shut on his head, cutting both his ears, and a nurse, who bending protectively over a baby in a cot, was struck in the rear by a large glass splinter. The explosion provoked Matron to wrath. She said, 'I have been chased by many strange things before but *never* by a door!'

During this dreadful night, and shortly after the explosion, two of the stretcher bearers, Major W. W. Neville and Mr Luigi Papa entered the tottering wreck of Cleland House and most bravely brought out a roof fire-watcher lying trapped in the wreckage. For this most daring feat they were both awarded the British Empire Medal. The Quarterly Board of Governors formally noted their 'most gallant services' on 23rd September 1941. At the same meeting they recorded with 'Pride and gratification' the exemplary behaviour of Nurse Gardner. Of such was the courage and devotion to duty of the Hospital and its staff. On that same night, a similar parachuted mine fell on the Grey Coat School and although it did not explode, the Board Room where the momentous meetings of 16th December 1719 to 20th April 1720 were held was completely destroyed, a curious commentary on the times.

When the dawn came the hospital was reduced to its lowest ebb. There were only some fifty beds serviceable and a very considerable amount of damage had been done. Yet recovery was rapid and the later air raids of the war in May 1941 and in February 1944 did no damage, nor did the V1 or V2 attacks, although alas, many patients were brought in. For the rest of the war the hospital and school functioned in their proper manner. It is fitting that a tribute should be paid here to the members of the staff who, horribly overworked, yet continued to keep up the

The Hospital at War, 1939–1945

G. T. Mullally, M.C. Assistant-Surgeon to Westminster 1920–27, Surgeon to Westminster 1937–50.

Sir Adolphe Abrahams, Dean of the Medical School 1934–43.

standards of the hospital. On the surgical side they were Mr Mullally, Mr Macnab, Mr Brockman and Mr E. S. Lee, and on the physicians side particularly, Dr Swithin Meadows, Dr W. E. Lloyd and Sir Adolphe Abrahams. The laboratory under Dr R. Magnus Haines continues its function, not only on the orthodox line of providing service to the hospital, the Westminster City Council and other bodies, but also a less orthodox one, for from 1938 to 1945 consignments of various vaccines for Messrs Genatosan were made in the laboratory. This was to help the small income of the school which has never been, alas, as highly endowed as other institutions. The most substantial, the 'John Burford Carlill Fund' was given

131

Westminster Home Guard.

by Mr A. J. H. Carlill in 1925 in memory of his father. The school consequently has had always to struggle against financial adversity. It is fitting here to note the prescience of the Director, R. J. V. Pulvertaft in 1938. Sensing the onset of war he laid in very large stocks of microscope slides, coverglasses, Petri dishes, and above all, agar-agar, the base of so many culture media. This enabled the laboratory to last out comfortably through the war when others got very short of these essential commodities. In the later years of the war conditions had so far returned to normal that the Annual Inaugural Ceremony was held again. In 1943 Mr Ernest Brown, the then Minister of Health, was the speaker, and in 1944 Sir John Fraser gave the Inaugural address.

In 1944 the hospital sent two surgical teams to the south coast in preparation for the 'D-day' landings. At first they were both stationed at the Queen Alexandra Hospital, Cosham, where they joined units from other hospitals. The Westminster contingent included Mr Stanley Lee, Dr R. Broad, Mr George Wynn Williams and the indefatigable 'Junior' G. Belyavin, now Professor of Bacteriology at University College. It only needs to be said that the 'Cosham Club' did a great deal of very valuable work and their services were highly valued.

The Party of Students leaving for Belsen 20th April 1945.

132

The Hospital at War, 1939–1945

Following the overrunning of the German concentration camp at Belsen it was decided to send teams of medical students to help to care for the unfortunate inmates. Accordingly, eleven students, fortunately very heavily immunised against typhoid, typhus and diphtheria, left the hospital on 28th April 1945 on their way to this frightful spot. There they worked hard and well and fully merited the praise given for their efforts. Their names were: George Woodwark, Derek Wells, Russell Barton, Eric Trimmer, R. E. Citrine, K. C. Easton, A. D. Moore, M. J. Hargrave, J. R. E. Jenkins, D. P. Bowler and L. K. Garstin.

If the students are mentioned thus, it is only fair to record the heroic efforts of the nursing staff, the hospital midwives who continued their district calls in the air raids, and those nurses and sisters who visited regularly a round of eleven deep shelters. One is especially proud to record that Nurse Scarlet, who trained at Westminster, received the George Cross for her work during the savage bombing of Portsmouth. It is sad to have to record here the deaths of Drs J. P. B. Ball, C. A. Moynihan and Surgeon-Lieutenant Wainright—killed in action; J. H. B. Round died on active service; Nurse Peggy Arnold, Ian Soutter and his father Dr Luther James Soutter and Thomas Cruttwell, were killed by flying-bomb attacks. Then, too, several members of the staff died during the war.

Mr Walter Spencer died in 1940, Dr David de Souza in 1942, Dr Hildred Carlill in 1942, Mr William Turner and Mr Arthur Griffith in 1944, and Sir Stanley Woodwark in 1945. They had all served Westminster well in their various ways and are thus worthy of our remembrance.

As the war drew to its end it was apparent that the practice of medicine and surgery in the years to come would be most vital and exciting. The advent of penicillin, the advances in knowledge of blood transfusion and intravenous therapy alone were sufficient to ensure that post-war conditions would be vastly different. Furthermore, there was talk, serious talk, of vast changes in the whole medical structure, the setting up of a State Medical Service and the abolition of the Voluntary Hospitals as they had been run in the past. At Westminster, the first hospital to be supported entirely by voluntary contributions from the public, such changes seemed impossible at the time. Other deeply thinking persons at this time also insisted that Westminster must, in the future, become much more closely allied to London University. How these changes came about is the theme of the next chapter.

Meanwhile, on V.E. Day plus one a most exhilarating and intoxicating dance was held. There was an uneasy pause, then bombs were dropped on Hiroshima and Nagasaki and this war, too, came to an end.

15
The End of the Beginning, 1945–1965

'The Chairman welcomed Professor Milne . . .'
Minutes of the Medical Committee, 1st May 1961

The latter part of 1945 seemed, at the time, most notable for the way people returned to their mother hospital: sisters, nurses, students and staff all came back, their return spread over several months; people who had been in many strange places and who were glad to be back at Westminster. Indeed, one function was held before the war ended, when the students who had been at the Staines County Hospital, in a pleasant atmosphere composed of beer, sausages and mash and much goodwill, thanked those gentlemen who had taught them. To these members of the staffs of other hospitals the students owed a great deal, and Mr Stephen, Dr Vines, Dr de Swiet, Mr Matheson, Mr Woodd-Walker, Dr Barham Carter, Dr Court, Dr Curtis, Dr Pratt, Mr MacLean, Dr Signy and, of course, Dr Maclagan and many others deserve the lasting gratitude of the schools for their efforts.

There were many tasks awaiting the hospital and school authorities. The damage to the building required attention and certain structural work not completed required to be done. For example, C and D theatres had never been equipped or used before the war began. Again, time had not permitted the opening of the entrance in Dean Ryle Street and, of course, the Page Street site was as yet unbuilt on. It was to take twenty years before the latter could be put in hand. Meanwhile, certain posts on the staff remained to be filled. There were four elections to the staff in 1946: Drs C. J. Gavey and F. D. Hart, and Messrs F. d'Abreu and D. Walker Ashcroft (E.N.T.) on the surgeons' side. In the school, R. J. V. Pulvertaft, who had been created O.B.E. for his services to the Army in the Middle East and who had attended Mr Churchill during his severe illness there, was made Professor in 1946. Characteristically, he chose the title of Professor of Clinical Pathology and set himself to direct the work of the laboratory into the three channels, Morbid Anatomy, Bacteriology and that new subject which had appeared, Haematology. Chemical Pathology remained a separate subject

The End of the Beginning, 1945–1965

under Dr Maclagan's sole control. In 1948 the University of London created a Chair of Chemical Pathology at Westminster and Dr Maclagan was installed as 'Professor of Chemical Pathology'. It was thus that the first Professors were created at Westminster. Two who returned to the staff after the war deserve special mention: they are, first, Arnold Stott, who had become a Major-General and returned as Sir Arnold Stott, K.B.E., and second, Stanford Cade, who had joined the R.A.F. at the onset of the war as a Squadron-Leader and rapidly rose to the distinguished heights of Air Vice-Marshal. For his services to the R.A.F. he was created, first, a Companion of the Bath and, later, a Knight Commander of the British Empire. But that was not all, for in 1940 he was elected a Member of the Royal College of Physicians. This was because he had written a most remarkable book, *Malignant Disease and Its Treatment by Radium*, which, with its many illustrations, was far in advance of its time. It is pleasant to recollect that a very large number of the photomicrographs in it were taken by the old senior technician, Mr Chopping, who Sir Stanford must have first met as a student.

In 1947 there were more appointments to the staff: Dr J. L. Lovibond (who had been one of Dr Carlill's House physicians) and Dr I. M. Anderson to take Dr Paterson's place. On the surgeon's side, Mr P. D. Trevor-Roper became Ophthalmic Surgeon and Mr Robert Cox, M.B.E. was made 4th Surgeon, the post first held by George James Guthrie.

One of the sad things about 1947 was the retirement of two of the really well-known members of the

hospital circle. The first of these was the Matron, Miss Edith Smith, O.B.E., R.R.C. Her term of office, thirty-two years, is the longest of all the nineteen Matrons to Westminster. The other to retire was Sir Adolphe Abrahams, O.B.E., who had been a member of the staff since 1920. He was a great teacher and a staunch supporter of all student functions, (not forgetting his contributions to *The Broadway*, the famous 'Unconsidered Trifles'). At this time, of course, there was, overshadowing all else, the National Health Services Act of 1946 which produced such fierce controversy and uncertainty as to its probable impact on the hospital and school. The authorities of each had, despite this, quietly acquired certain property. The hospital had been given most generously by Mr Margary, the house, Chartham Park, for use as a convalescent home. It was formally opened on 1st May 1946 with Miss Prior, for many years Assistant Matron at Westminster, installed as Matron. The property was honoured on 4th April by a visit from Her Majesty, Queen Mary, who showed keen interest in this project. The school, on the other hand, had acquired a property much nearer to hand and for a different purpose. This was Brabazon House in Moreton Street, S.W.1 for use as a students' hostel, a most useful acquisition.

Two other features of school life at this time may be mentioned—the admittance once again of women students, in 1946, and the establishment under Dr Peter Hansell of the Medical Photographic Department. The contribution of the latter to the school and hospital has been so great that it is not at all surprising

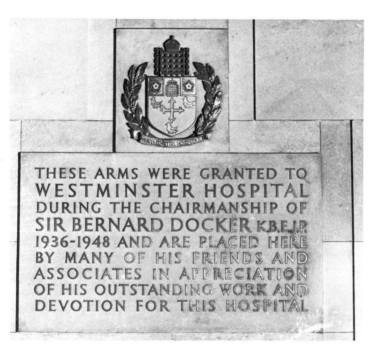

The plaque in the Entrance Hall commemorating the services of Sir Bernard Docker to Westminster.

THESE ARMS WERE GRANTED TO WESTMINSTER HOSPITAL DURING THE CHAIRMANSHIP OF SIR BERNARD DOCKER K.B.E.J.P. 1936-1948 AND ARE PLACED HERE BY MANY OF HIS FRIENDS AND ASSOCIATES IN APPRECIATION OF HIS OUTSTANDING WORK AND DEVOTION FOR THIS HOSPITAL

to record that its staff have, over the years, won practically all the prizes and awards possible in this field.

Finally, and despite the protests and plebiscites of the B.M.A. the dreaded day arrived. It was the 5th July 1948—the 'vesting day' of the National Health Act. The Author was in Erskine Ward at about 3 p.m.

investigating a patient when the tea-trolley arrived. Two gentlemen opposite woke up, dived into their lockers and produced their pots of jam for their bread and butter. A few minutes later a junior member of the catering staff entered carrying a tray of little cakes which he offered to them 'How much?' said the senior of this pair, suspiciously. 'With the compliments of the Governors,' said the cake-bearer. 'Well,' said the patient, 'this beats cock-fighting.' It was in this way that the National Health Act made its impact on Erskine Ward.

There were, of course, very many changes made, especially in the administration of the hospital at this time, and one of these was a sad but inevitable happening. It was clear that the Minister of Health, Mr Aneurin Bevan, would not designate Sir Bernard Docker as Chairman of the Board of Governors because Sir Bernard was much opposed to the National Health Scheme. On hearing of this Sir Bernard resigned from the Board and the Minister appointed Lord Nathan, the then Vice-Chairman, as Chairman of the Board of Governors. As a grant of arms had just been made to the hospital the plaque in the entrance hall was erected, as it says, by some of his friends to commemorate this fact and to keep alive the memory of Sir Bernard who was Chairman during so many vital and dangerous years of the hospital's life. Under the new régime the hospital as a Teaching Hospital found itself at the centre of what is known as the South-West Metropolitan Region and several other smaller hospitals were 'designated', as the phrase was, as coming under the control of the Board. These were the

The End of the Beginning, 1945–1965

Infants' Hospital (now the Westminster Children's Hospital) and the Gordon Hospital in Vincent Square, and also the All Saints' Hospital in Austell Street, Lambeth. It is often a source of surprise that the Grosvenor Hospital for Women in Vincent Square was not designated to the Westminster Group. This hospital at the time, however, was already affiliated to St Thomas's.

All Saints' Hospital, strangely enough, was tied already by a sentimental thread to Westminster. Its principal founder was Mr Canny Ryall, who was an old Westminster student who had indeed been Surgical Registrar in 1899.

At this time also, the convalescent home at Parkwood and the Yarrow convalescent home came into the Hospital Group. The total number of beds in the group was, therefore, as follows—

	Beds
Westminster Hospital	427
Westminster Children's Hospital	78
Gordon Hospital	102
All Saints' Hospital	50
Parkwood	114
The Yarrow Home	60
Chartham Park	30
Total	861

It was estimated that the cost of running these would be in the order of £900,000 (1949). At this time, also, the hospital took over the Empire Nursing Home in Vincent Square and, later, other properties, to house the vast increases in nursing staff needed for the new commitments of modern medicine. The coming of the National Health Service produced a great change in the status of the consultant staff, for they now became salaried employees of the Minister of Health whereas, of course, before the Act they worked for the honour of being a member of the staff. Indeed, the only 'Honoraries' left were those who worked for the University of London and had honorary contracts with the Ministry so as to be able to see and treat patients.

On 13th July 1949 the Centenary of the opening of the Medical School was celebrated. It was a great honour to be visited on this occasion once more by the Earl of Athlone who had opened the new Medical School in May 1938. It may be asked how were the students getting on in the new Medical School since the war ended? The answer is very well indeed, both scholastically, socially and in the realm of sport. In this connexion the Tennis VI were the first to show the way—in 1949 they played ten matches and won them all. In addition, they won the Inter-hospital Championship Cup beating St Thomas's in the final, and the Inter-hospital Singles Championship, beating Guy's. They also won the London University Cup, beating Imperial College in the final, and the London University Singles Cup, beating in the final the London School of Economics. The team was D. H. Mackenzie (Capt.), C. C. Cox, W. S. Goodman, R. F. Lowe, R. Grande and N. R. (Tim) Lewis, who had the honour of playing for England in the Davis

Cup. (I must point out that the two singles cups were won by D. H. Mackenzie, as Tim Lewis was not able to compete in either.) The years from 1947 onwards show, in fact, a most remarkable excellence in all branches of sport, be it Rugby football, tennis, cricket, rowing and rifle shooting to name a few. A highlight was the winning of the Silver Goblets and Nicholls Challenge Cup at Henley in 1952 by H. C. I. Bywaters and T. H. Christie when they beat the forty-year-old record!

It was in 1949 that a very significant step was taken which required some boldness of thought at the time. The lower ground floor of the hospital had been divided among three special departments. the Diagnostic Radiology Department, the Department of Physical Medicine, and the Radiotherapy Department. The last-named department had, of course, its radium sources and conventional X-ray therapy sets. They had also the confidence and ability to handle more powerful sources. In 1948 it was decided to purchase a 2-million electron-volt van de Graaff generator in America, and to find space for this Dr Beaumont most generously gave up part of the space used as a gymnasium in the Department of Physical Medicine. This instrument proved its worth as soon as it was put into service. To continue with this subject, strictly out of chronological order, it may be said that when the radium sources were called in in favour of radioactive cobalt in 1957, Mr Michael Wix most generously gave a large sum of money to install one of these very powerful sources. To accommodate this in 1957 the Governors (with the concurrence of

Dr Beaumont, of course) built a temporary Physical Medicine Department on the vacant Page Street site. This enabled the Radiotherapy Department to extend and to install a so-called 'caesium mass' unit in 1958, and another giant radioactive cobalt device in 1960. In 1960, also, the 6½-million electron-volt linear accelerator was installed, thus providing the department with sources of treatment suitable for every type of case requiring radiotherapy.

To return to the more strict order of chronology is to find that Miss G. Ceris Jones, who had followed Miss Smith as the Matron in 1948, decided to leave us to return to the London Hospital. This was in late 1950. Miss Jones's short stay as Matron had been at a very difficult time—those in charge of nursing administration owe her a deep debt of gratitude. She was, of course, succeeded in office by Miss Lavinia Young, whose proud title became 'Matron to Westminster Hospital and Nursing Adviser to the Board'.

Dominating all other events in 1951 was the illness of the hospital Patron, H.M. King George VI. This is not the place nor the time to say more than has been said previously, except to add that all those from the hospital who came in contact with His Majesty felt a deep sense of personal grief and loss at his so sudden and untimely death in January 1952. Their names can be read on the beautiful window in the hospital chapel.

In late 1951 there was added to the chapel its famous altar-piece 'The Resurrection' by Veronese. Its acquisition was due to the Reverend Christopher Hildyard who saw it up for sale at £12,000. It is said

The Chapel, showing the Veronese altar piece 'The Resurrection'.

that he offered £10,000 for it and coolly asked for it to be delivered the next day! The purchase price was found equally between the Board of Governors and certain generous outside benefactors. At a Service of Dedication on 14th November 1952, presided over by the Dean of Westminster, it was unveiled by the President of the Royal Academy, Sir Gerald Kelly.

The 'King's Window' in the Chapel.

At this service also, three memorial windows were solemnly dedicated. The first was presented to the chapel by Mary, Countess Harcourt; the second, given by the late W. J. R. Elgy Esq., was to commemorate those citizens of Westminster who died in the two World Wars; the third, the children's window, was given by the League of St Nicholas and commemorates the work of children for the hospital. These beautiful additions to the chapel are a source of inspiration to all those who worship there and an abiding memorial to those who gave so much to the hospital.

The years had not passed without inevitable changes in the staff. These sometimes seem to occur in what the epidemiologists call 'clusters'. Such a year was 1950, for in its passing both Sir Arnold Stott and Mr G. T. Mullally retired and Mr Macnab gave up his office as Dean. The retirement of Mr Mullally enabled yet another Westminster student, Mr C. E. Drew, M.V.O. to be elected to the staff. The vacancy caused by Sir Arnold Stott's retirement was filled by Dr R. D. Tonkin; Mr H. E. Harding took office as Dean. Mr Macnab's term of office could not have been held at a more difficult time. Posterity will regard him with affection as one of the great Deans of the school.

The year 1953 was, of course, Coronation Year—the medical arrangements inside the Abbey fell yet again to the hospital. They were in the capable hands of Mr Harding and, of course, were most efficiently carried out. This year also, another Patron of the hospital, Her Majesty Queen Mary, died. She had been Patroness from 1930 to 1953 and had taken a very great interest in the hospital. The Queen Mary Nurses' Home will be an abiding memorial to this truly great figure.

The nurses' home had been honoured by a visit from Queen Elizabeth the Queen Mother on 12th February 1953, when Her Majesty graciously presented the prizes at the annual ceremony. It was a red-letter day for the nurses' home.

Of the many years of triumph and disaster in the decade 1950–60, 1954 must be considered pre-eminent. It began on a happy note, for Miss P. Wheatley, the Superintendent Radiographer to the Radiotherapy Department, was awarded the M.B.E. in the New Year's Honours. No one deserved an honour more as a reward for so many years of devoted service. Then on the 6th March Mr Charles M. Power, O.B.E., M.C. died. He had been Secretary and House Governor since 1921. A man of great integrity as Lord Nathan said, 'He was passionately devoted to Westminster.' He was a quiet man with great personal courage, as his Military Cross indicated; during the dreadful night of 16th April 1941 after the land-mine fell, he personally went on the roof of the hospital and stayed there as roof watcher for a considerable period of time. He was succeeded by Mr R. I. G. Brooks. Another tragedy struck the hospital in May, for on the 4th Dr J. L. Lovibond died suddenly and most unexpectedly on his 47th birthday. This was a great loss for 'Jock' Lovibond was dear to the hearts of staff and students alike. Dr R. I. S. Bayliss was elected to fill the staff vacancy in his place.

The End of the Beginning, 1945–1965

Later in the year Mr Aubrey Goodwin, O.B.E., M.D., F.R.C.S. retired. He was the Senior Gynaecologist, shrewd, debonair and the acknowledged master of his craft. He was well known for his wit. When green sterile towels were introduced in the theatre practice, he retaliated by appearing in a red cap and mask with blue boots. This colour scheme he wore to the end of his hospital career. Mr Goodwin was one of the two members of the staff I have been able to discover who have had to do with elephants. Mr Goodwin shot one in the thirties; the other gentleman, Mr Nottidge Charles Macnamara fell off his on to the body of a dead tiger. To complete the record, Mr Goodwin's elephant was African, Mr Macnamara's was Indian. Mr Goodwin's place on the staff was filled by Mr R. de Vere.

Another event of 1954 was the opening of the new sports ground at Cobham by Mr H. M. Abrahams on Saturday, 3rd July. This was the first sports ground ever owned by the Medical School. Its acquisition was undoubtedly due to the Dean who, finding that the District Valuer could not agree on a value for the University, persuaded the Board of Governors to buy it and lease it to the school on a 99-years' lease.

In 1955 an important event took place: the Vincent Square Laboratories in Vauxhall Bridge Road were opened by the Chairman of the Board of Governors, Lord Nathan. These laboratories have most worthily served their function, and it was a most far-sighted proposal at that time to have built them. Indeed, it is surprising to the uninitiated to realise at times quite how far ahead the authorities are looking. A case in

Sir Ivan Magill, K.C.V.O. *Sir Clement Price Thomas, K.C.V.O.*

point is the 'Ice Rink Site' as it is called, that is, the old Westminster Ice Rink. This building was acquired by the school against the future in 1952. It figures largely in present plans, and is now a car park.

The end of the decade was marked by the retirement of four 'giants' of Westminster. These were, of course, Ivan Magill in 1953, Sir Clement Price

141

Sir Stanford Cade, K.B.E., C.B.   *Dr W. E. Lloyd.*

after a short illness, on the morning of the 23rd. It was a great tragedy that a man so young and of such integrity should die so soon after his appointment. He was followed in this most onerous and important office by the present House Governor, Mr Patrick MacMahon. The Wolfson School is a most up-to-date and functional building and possesses a most beautiful library named in memory of the late Edwina Lady Mountbatten, who nursed as a V.A.D. nurse in the hospital during the war. It is thus that progress occurs in hospital matters for this building is a far cry from Queen Anne's Gate!

It was also in 1960 that a further development in school affairs began. For several years, debate as to the merits (or otherwise) of professorial units in medicine and surgery had occurred. The matter was brought to a head following the stern quinquennial visit of a section of the University Grants Committee. It was, alas, that after meeting this body that Sir Ernest Rock Carling died in the night, serving his old school and hospital to the last breath in his body. The

Thomas in 1958 and Sir Stanford Cade in 1960. That much-loved physician, Dr W. E. Lloyd, whose career so closely paralleled Sir Clement's, retired in 1959.

Towards the end of 1958 it was announced that the Wolfson Trust were advancing a sum of £250,000 to build a nurses' training school. The building went ahead well and was formally opened on Thursday, 23rd March 1960, by H.M. Queen Elizabeth the Queen Mother. The day, however, was marred by grief for the death of Mr R. I. G. Brooks, O.B.E., M.A.,

The Wolfson School of Nursing, opened 23rd March 1960 by H.M. the Queen Mother.

St John's, Westminster, whose burial ground was St John's Gardens. Designed by Thomas Archer and built 1713–28.

School Council, headed now by Lord Fleck, who took over from Mr H. R. P. Hoare, who had acted for a short time as Chairman after the death, in 1956, of Mr Clowes (who had held this office from 1935 until his death) made the decision to appoint a Professor of Medicine. The successful candidate was Professor M. D. Milne. It was necessary to reorganise the beds in the hospital to accommodate this medical unit and all credit is due to the unselfish way members of the staff underwent this sacrifice. It was well worth while, for the whole of the teaching was electrified by this appointment.

In 1962, two further Chairs were created, of Surgery and of Bacteriology. To the Surgical Chair, Professor Harold Ellis was appointed, and Dr B. W. Lacey was appointed Professor of Bacteriology. Nor was this all, for Dr A. D. Morgan had conferred on him the title of 'Professor of Morbid Anatomy'. Sir

Geoffrey Organe was created Professor of Anaesthetics in 1966, and Mr Peter Curzen was created Professor of Obstetrics and Gynaecology in 1970.

In 1960 the Governors 'acquired' in the Westminster Group, Queen Mary's Hospital, Roehampton. This hospital's large site includes a Burns Unit of the Regional Board, the famous limb-fitting centre and its factory and an historic mansion, Roehampton House. Designed by Thomas Archer in 1712 and built for Thomas Cary, this building is one of the most attractive of the few remaining examples of Archer's work. Another, by coincidence, is St John's Church (1713–28) in Smith Square, hard by Westminster Hospital itself.

Roehampton House ('The Mansion'). Designed by Thomas Archer 1712, with additions by Sir Edwin Lutyens.

Miss Lavinia Young, Matron to Westminster 1951–66 and Nursing Adviser to the Board of Governors.

On acquiring Queen Mary's it was necessary to obtain the General Nursing Council's permission to train student nurses there. Miss Young was so successful in persuading her trained staff to go there, and in obtaining a full number of student nurses to be taught, that her unstinting efforts deserve our deepest thanks.

Westminster Hospital 1716–1974

In these days hospitals require nursing staff of the highest possible standards. That we have them, 1,200 in all, in the Group, shows the regard placed in the School of Nursing and its staff by the public at large.

The acquisition of Roehampton has led to many anxious discussions on the future of Westminster. Before this subject is raised, however, two other individual events deserve our attention. The first was the election of Mr A. C. H. Bell as President of the Royal College of Obstetricians and Gynaecologists in 1963. This was a signal honour, most worthily deserved. Mr Bell had served the hospital from the early thirties, first as Registrar and then as a member of the staff. He is a most popular teacher and took (and still takes) a very keen interest in the student clubs and functions.

In 1963 the hospital and school suffered a most grievous loss in the death of Lord Nathan, who had served the hospital for so many years, both as Vice-Chairman and later as Chairman of the Board of Governors. Lord Nathan was very proud of the hospital and especially of its connexion with the Houses of Parliament which has come about over the years. 'Parliament's own Hospital' was a phrase often on his lips. It was especially fitting that when the Page Street building was finally begun the foundation stone was laid by Eleanor, Lady Nathan in 1964. This building on the Page Street site had been the subject of much discussion over the years and many plans had been made and discarded. The Page Street committee and its indomitable Chairman, Dr Gavey, were at last given the news that progress was to take place and it is fitting to applaud the constant efforts put forward

144

by the post-war Deans, Mr Macnab, Mr Harding and Dr Bayliss, who succeeded Mr Harding in this office in 1960 and served until 1964 when he gave up the post because of illness. His successor, Dr J. B. Wyman, M.B.E., is, oddly enough, only the third old Westminster student to be Dean. The others were Sir Ernest Rock Carling 1910–11 and Dr Gossage in

Lord Nathan, P.C., D.C.L., F.S.A., Chairman of the Board of Governors 1948–63.

Foundation Stone of Page Street Wing laid by Lady Eleanor Nathan on 2nd November 1964.

Left: *The Page Street Building.* Below: *Cross-section showing its departments and connexion to hospital.*

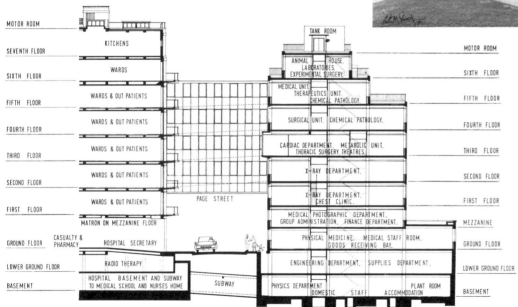

| WESTMINSTER HOSPITAL (EXISTING) | | NEW PAGE STREET BUILDING |

MOTOR ROOM

SEVENTH FLOOR — KITCHENS

SIXTH FLOOR — WARDS

FIFTH FLOOR — WARDS & OUT PATIENTS

FOURTH FLOOR — WARDS & OUT PATIENTS

THIRD FLOOR — WARDS & OUT PATIENTS

SECOND FLOOR — WARDS & OUT PATIENTS

FIRST FLOOR — WARDS & OUT PATIENTS

MATRON ON MEZZANINE FLOOR

PAGE STREET

GROUND FLOOR — CASUALTY & PHARMACY — HOSPITAL SECRETARY

LOWER GROUND FLOOR — RADIO THERAPY

BASEMENT — HOSPITAL BASEMENT AND SUBWAY TO MEDICAL SCHOOL AND NURSES HOME — SUBWAY

TANK ROOM

MOTOR ROOM

ANIMAL HOUSE. LABORATORIES. EXPERIMENTAL SURGERY. — SIXTH FLOOR

MEDICAL UNIT. THERAPEUTICS UNIT. CHEMICAL PATHOLOGY. — FIFTH FLOOR

SURGICAL UNIT. CHEMICAL PATHOLOGY. — FOURTH FLOOR

CARDIAC DEPARTMENT. METABOLIC UNIT. THORACIC SURGERY THEATRES. — THIRD FLOOR

X-RAY DEPARTMENT. — SECOND FLOOR

X-RAY DEPARTMENT. CHEST CLINIC. — FIRST FLOOR

MEDICAL PHOTOGRAPHIC DEPARTMENT. GROUP ADMINISTRATION. FINANCE DEPARTMENT. — MEZZANINE

PHYSICAL MEDICINE. MEDICAL STAFF ROOM. GOODS RECEIVING BAY. — GROUND FLOOR

ENGINEERING DEPARTMENT. SUPPLIES DEPARTMENT. — LOWER GROUND FLOOR

PHYSICS DEPARTMENT. DOMESTIC STAFF ACCOMMODATION. PLANT ROOM — BASEMENT

The End of the Beginning, 1945—1965

1902–03. It is fair to state that the hospital has taken as much effort as the school; the late Lord Nathan had spent many years endeavouring to move the Ministry of Health in this matter, and the present Chairman, Sir John Vaughan-Morgan, now Lord Reigate, has been equally interested in its completion.

In 1963, also, a most popular member of the staff, Mr Walker Dudley Ashcroft, the E.N.T. surgeon, died. He had been for many years a stout upholder of student activities and was justly renowned for his ability as a teacher and his dexterity as a surgeon. His loss was deeply felt by his colleagues and friends.

As 1965 drew to its close, the Hospital once again had to face its historical dilemma, to move (*see* 1830, 1912, 1919), in this case to Roehampton, or to stay in Westminster and build a District Hospital at Roehampton with improved teaching facilities there as well. How the Hospital and School faced this eternal problem and others even more formidable are described later. Yet, as the 250th anniversary of the Hospital's inception drew near, still one felt the spirit of compassion that inspired Mr Henry Hoare, when he told Mr Robert Witham, Mr William Wogan and the Reverend Patrick Cockburn that 'he had £10 in his hands'.

16
Kelly's Orange

'The Queen visited Westminster Hospital this afternoon.'
Court Circular, 19th October 1966

January 14th 1966 was a clear day but very cold. A bitter wind scourged the cheeks of the groups of old friends who met outside the West Door of the Abbey and drove them thankfully into the interior. The Abbey itself was a brilliant sight as it, too, was celebrating its own 900th centenary that year. As the Abbey filled the tension among the spectators was steadily built up. There were processions of the Consultant Staff in their gowns in two lines led by the Dean, Dr J. B. Wyman, and the Chairman of the Medical Committee, Mr G. H. Macnab. (A cynic said he had never seen the staff properly dressed and all going in the same direction ever before.) There were processions of the Registrars, of the Senior Nursing Staff, and of the guests who had come to honour the Hospital. These dignitaries, led by the Vice-Chancellor of London University, were in the main conducted to their seats by venerable gentlemen macebearers; an exception was the President of the College of Pathologists, led to *his* seat by Dr John Stafford bearing the College's very simple mace—a touching gesture. Then came the Directors General of the Armed Forces and their Matrons in Chief, the St John Ambulance Brigade and the British Red Cross Society. Then came the two Vice-Patrons, The Speaker and the Lord Chancellor, followed by the Mayor of Westminster. Now came the Clergy, the Hospital Chaplains, followed by the Bishop of Kensington and the stately figure of the Cardinal Archbishop of Westminster. Then, finally, the Procession of the Church of Westminster, the cross carried by David Scott.

The service itself presented many memorable moments, the singing of the choir led and organised by Dr Reeves, the fanfares of the R.A.M.C. Trumpeters, the Lessons read by the Chairman and by the Matron, and the moving address by the Dean of Westminster. But the most impressive moment to many was the Hospital Prayer read by the Dean—

148

Met together to commemorate with thanksgiving before Almighty God the inception of Westminster Hospital 250 years ago . . . .

After the Service, the bells of the Abbey church were rung and the congregation dispersed.

After a series of luncheons in Church House, an Historical Symposium was held in the Assembly Hall and before this was opened by the Minister of Health, the Rt Honourable Kenneth Robinson, M.P., the following message from Her Majesty the Queen was read by the Chairman of the Board.

'I send to the Board of Governors and to all the staff of Westminster Hospital my congratulations and best wishes on the successful celebration of the 250th Anniversary of the beginning of the Hospital of

The staff in procession, Anniversary Service, Westminster Abbey 14th January 1966.

149

Historical display, Anniversary celebrations, Church House, Westminster 14th January 1966.

which I am Patron. I am proud of the association of my family with this great teaching hospital over so many years and I am sensible of the medical and nursing services which have been given to the members of the Royal Family from time to time. I know that the tradition of service to the sick continues and is indeed being expanded. The completion of the new extension of the Hospital in due course will bring the greatest satisfaction to all.'

The Symposium was then opened by the Minister. Mr Rennie Hoare spoke of his famous ancestor, Henry Hoare, and the Author then gave a dissertation on the Hospital's history; during which, overcome by the event, he brandished one of the keys of the Iron Chest in the direction of the St George's representative, laid it down, and forgot it! Hours later, the horrified speaker found that Mr Wickings had seen the incident and taken care of it!

The Symposium (which was continued by demonstrations the next day) was followed by a celebration banquet at the London Hilton Hotel. There were nearly one thousand guests, the guest of honour being 'Mr Speaker' (the Rt Hon. Dr Horace King) who gave a masterful speech. The evening, however, was dedicated to, and dominated by, the meeting of old friends.

There were further festivities during the year, film shows in April and May, including a silent film made about the Hospital in 1927, and evening parties in the Dean's garden at the Abbey in June. The year led on to the Queen's unofficial visit on 18th October. Her

Presentation of a copy of the first edition to H.M. Queen Elizabeth, October 19th 1966. (Sport and General News)

Majesty visited some of the wards and departments of the Hospital and took tea in the Queen Mary Nurses' Home. After tea, long-serving members of the staff were presented to Her Majesty who was graciously pleased to accept a copy of the first edition of this History and also a set of the silver and bronze 250th Anniversary commemoration medallions, presented by Student Nurse Rosalind Barton.

There were two resignations during the year to which reference must be made. The first was that of

250th Anniversary commemoration medallions in silver and bronze.

Miss Marjorie Mudge, Chief Nursing Officer to the Westminster Group of Hospitals from November 1966.

Sir Geoffrey Shakespeare, who had been on the Board of Governors since 1947 and had been Vice-Chairman of the Board from 1948–63. The second was of Miss Lavinia Young, Matron of Westminster Hospital for 15 years and Nursing Adviser to the Board. Miss Young was the last of the 'old style' Westminster Matrons, for the task of co-ordinating the work and training of a staff of more than one thousand was a gigantic one. The Ministry of Health had recognised the strains so placed in large hospital groups and had adopted the Report of the Committee on Senior Nursing Staff Structure headed by Mr Brian Salmon, the Vice-Chairman of the Board. After the resignation of Miss Young, the Board decided to appoint a Chief Nursing Officer, Miss Marjorie Mudge, to be free to organise nursing policy development throughout the Group. A further development of 1966 was the setting up of the Westminster Hospital Research Trust; its chairman Lord Erroll of Hale put immense energy into the new venture.

1967 began with one pleasant piece of news, for Miss Young was created O.B.E. in the New Year's Honours List, a richly deserved award. But alas, the Hospital and School suffered a grievous loss by the death of Mr G. H. Macnab on 1st March 1967. George Macnab joined the Hospital in 1930. He became the Medical

151

George Macnab, Surgeon to Westminster 1937–67.

Superintendent of the Hospital in 1940 and also took on the burden of Dean of the Medical School at the same time. It is due to him that the School continued its active teaching functions at this dangerous time, for there were not wanting those who would have closed the School and 'designated' the buildings for other functions. He resisted these efforts and his reward was to see the School and the Hospital rise to even greater

eminence in the post-war years. We all owe him an everlasting debt of gratitude as a selfless leader, a man of great integrity and a friend to Westminster and all who worked there. During 1967 everyone waited with growing impatience the building of the Page Street extension, but difficulties arose so that it was not until 24th June 1968 that the building was finally opened officially by the Minister of Health. This was a source of great gratification to us all. It finally crowned all the long years of hard work that Dr C. J. Gavey (Mr Page Street) had put into it. *Finis coronat opus.* With the perversity of things inanimate, a 2-inch water pipe on the second floor ruptured two hours after a select band of Consultants had toured the building one Saturday morning just before the opening was scheduled to take place. The new extension was speedily occupied by those eagerly awaiting this new space, and the Westminster buildings were thus completed 33 years after they had first been started. It was soon seen that the new buildings had a character, perhaps an inbuilt impishness entirely of their own, for the X-ray department film store jammed, and the Professor of Medicine found that to approach his new office in a lighthearted or casual way was to receive the most fierce static electrical shocks that could be imagined! But time soon healed these jars and frictions! The effect of these new departments on the efficiency of the Hospital and School was immense.

The Birthday Honours List of 1968 brought a most pleasant and richly deserved reward to Professor Geoffrey Organe, who was created Knight Bachelor for his untiring services to Anaesthesia, not only to

152

Kelly's Orange

anaesthesia in England (he is adviser to the Department ment of Health) but throughout the world. There is hardly any country that he has not visited on behalf of this specialty. His friends and colleagues all basked in the reflected glory of this award. During all this time developments were taking place at Roehampton, which had also a marked effect on the efficiency of the Group as a whole. The first of these was the opening of the new Obstetric Unit to patients in January 1968. This splendid new unit, custom built for its purpose, functioned flawlessly from the beginning, both from the patients' point of view and from the nurses and doctors also. So, too, was the opening of the new

The new Obstetric Unit, Queen Mary's, Roehampton, opened January 1968.

Department of Oral Surgery, a tribute to Mr Rupert Sutton-Taylor's determination. It replaced a hut that was so old that its equipment included a full set of enamel buckets to catch the rain on wet days! 1968, however, brought its changes also, one of which requires mention; that was the proposal to discontinue the House Committee, which took place finally on 14th January 1969. This came about because of the very great changes that had overtaken Hospital management in the post war years. From its earliest days, Hospital affairs had been conducted by the Board of Trustees (later Board of Governors). There were weekly Boards and Quarterly Boards. Alas, as the institution grew in size and complexity regular Committees became necessary, and executive decisions had to be delegated to a much smaller unit than the Board. It must be realised that in those days the payment of the yearly subscription meant that the Trustee could vote at Board meetings so that the decisions taken at one meeting were frequently reversed at the next by organised opposition which 'packed' the meeting. It was not until 1826 that the Medical Committee was formed. The first Secretary to the Board, Mr Wilson, was appointed in 1833 and the House Committee was first appointed in 1835. Under such chairmen as Sir Rutherford Alcock and Sir Bernard Docker decisions, when arrived at, were presented to the Board of Governors with such force and cogency that the Board had no option but to pass them. Sometimes, however, the House Committee was faced with 'peculiar cases'. In 1937, for example, the residents were presented at dinner with a huge cube

of weeping, cracked, and dishevelled cheese. An affronted House Surgeon seized it and uttering a strange Manx oath, threw it out of the window whence it fell into the area below to strike the storekeeper on the head. He, not unnaturally, was aggrieved and reported the incident to the House Governor, Mr Power. Mr Power reported it to the House Committee, who discussed it very seriously for some little time until they dissolved into helpless laughter when Mr Carling said, 'I don't see what all the fuss is about, when *I* was House Surgeon I threw a leg of mutton out of the same window and hit a policeman. Nobody complained about *that*.'

There was a sad ceremony on 29th June 1948 (the week before the vesting date of the National Health Act); the Board of Governors met for the last time under the President, Lord Wigram and having abolished the House Committee, solemnly and formally yielded up their powers by dissolving themselves. On July 6th the new Board appointed by the Minister of Health met for the first time under their new Chairman, Lord Nathan. They appointed a Finance Committee and a new House Committee, which as required by the Act, had no control over finance and could not take executive decisions. Over the years the sphere of usefulness of the House Committee declined until it was decided to wind it up in 1968. During the years 1968–70, a most thorough study of the Group's resources was made by the Board utilising the services of Professor Jacque's team from Brunel University and a firm of Management Consultants, Messrs Booz, Allen. Their recommendations touched every department of the

154

Kelly's Orange

Hospital and its administration. In so far as the medical staff were concerned, another event which touched them all took place. This was the institution of the 'Cogwheel' system of divisional committees (of physicians, surgeons, pathologists, etc) whose chairmen form with others a Medical Executive Committee. The recommendations of this Committee go to the Executive Committee of the Board of Governors. This has left the Medical Committee (now the Group Medical Committee) as a forum for debate where 'what touches all shall be approved by all'.

As 1969 drew on, a serious event occurred in the Page Street building, no less than a fire in the lift motor building on the roof. Watching the activities of the firemen in their crested helmets on the roof, one was irresistably reminded of an attack on a fort by Red Indians! The next minute the illusion was complete, for having attacked the metal sheeting with his axe one of them laid hand to the hot metal and burst into a war dance! More seriously, however, the animals on the sixth floor were in grave danger from the fire and smoke. They were most courageously rescued by Mr Rowe Jones (then a Surgical Registrar) and the Hospital Secretary, Mr Ian Robertson. For their services they were commended formally by the Board. It is only fair to say that the fire was most expeditiously put out in a very short time indeed.

It is sad to relate that the Hospital Group suffered a grave loss by the death, in a car accident, in August 1969, of Lady Gamage. All of us who had the privilege of knowing her know how much she had the welfare of the Children's Hospital and the Students at heart.

Throughout the history of the Hospital and the School one is struck by the selfless service given by voluntary workers like Lady Gamage and, indeed, by the dedicated services of the officers of the Board as well. Such a one is Mr Eric Gower who formally retired from his office in November 1969. He had joined the staff as Accountant in 1930, and became Financial Secretary a little later when, under Mr Power, he was responsible not only for the disbursement of money but also for its collection. As at that time the Hospital was planning its move to St Johns Gardens, this was an onerous and responsible task indeed. He later became Finance Officer and, later still, Treasurer. The day after he retired he received a letter from the Board offering him the post of Archivist, which he at present holds. As the Hospital 'treasures' had been dispersed into little rooms and odd cupboards his new task was of 'detective' and 'deductive' in method. Only he knew where Mr So-and-So would have put pictures and archives 30 years previously. Now our Archives are in splendid order, and many of them, especially the Minute Books, have been deposited for safe keeping with the Greater London Council. 1970 was a year of many structural changes in the Hospital, for the space vacated by the opening of the Page Street Buildings was rapidly converted. Thus, the Haematology and Blood Transfusion Departments were gathered up from five tiny rooms and housed in the lower ground floor of the Hospital. At the same time the Special Departments were refurbished. A recovery room was built for the main Theatres by displacing Professor Mackenzie (and the Chaplain), Professor Mackenzie

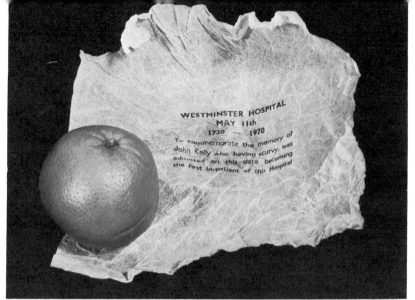

Kelly's Orange, 11th May 1970.

to a penthouse on the roof, the Chaplain to an en-larged and superior vestry. A generous donor also paid for fitting out a Simulator room in the Radio-therapy Department. This has enabled even more

Westminster Hospital 1716–1974

accurate (were it possible) measurement of field size and dose distribution in patients undergoing radiation. Yet the historical event of *this* year was the 250th Anniversary of the admission of the first in-patient on 11th May, 1720. As he, John Kelly, was admitted with 'Evil in his joints and scurvy' from which he was cured by that ex-mariner Dr Stuart, a special effort was called for. The Board decreed that every in-patient was to be given an orange wrapped in a commemorative wrapper, and this was done. The Author (assisted by Mr Gower of course) put on show many of the new-found treasures in the Board Room, an exhibition which was very heavily attended, especially by the younger members of the staff. Yet overhanging, as it were, all these parochial events were two black clouds which promised most certainly to alter all that had gone before and might even threaten the very future of the Group itself. Yet before these matters are discussed, it shall be recorded that the whole Group showed their delight at a signal honour granted to the Chairman of the Board. In the Birthday Honours he was created a Life Peer, taking the title of Lord Reigate, a fitting reward to his services on our behalf.

156

17
A Salvo of Reports

'The sly shade of an Urban Dean.'

Grantchester?

Hardly had the Page Street building been opened when the School authorities were faced with the first Report. This was the Report on Medical Education, called after its Chairman, Lord Todd, the 'Todd Report'. This made many recommendations that touched on the education of medical students and postgraduates and also suggested fundamental changes in the Teaching Hospital structure, and its organisation in London particularly. Briefly, as regards student education the pre-clinical period was to be lengthened and the students should proceed to a B.Sc. degree. The content of the syllabus should include in these early studies elementary pathology, statistics, genetics, psychiatry, and social studies of the type now referred to as 'Community Medicine'. The Report suggested that every effort should be made to attain *this* ideal state— (Section 200 of the Report). 'We take the view, therefore, that the aim of medical education should be to produce at graduation, a person with two essential qualifications. He should have, first, a knowledge of the medical and behavioural sciences sufficient for him to understand the scientific basis of his profession and to permit him to go forward with medicine as it develops further; and, second, by a general introduction to clinical method and patient care in the main branches of medicine and surgery, together with an introduction to social and preventive medicine.'

The Report proposed that the twelve London Teaching Hospitals should be grouped together in appropriate geographical pairs, each pair linked to a multi-faculty university institution. The linkings suggested were: St Bartholomew's Hospital and The London Hospital with Queen Mary College; University College Hospital Medical School and Royal Free Hospital School of Medicine with University College; Guy's Hospital Medical School and King's College Hospital Medical School with King's College; St Mary's Hospital Medical School and The Middlesex Hospital Medical School with Bedford College; St Thomas's Hospital Medical School and St George's

Hospital Medical School with a new multi-faculty institution. Westminster was paired with Charing Cross and linked to Imperial College. Much debate took place concerning these staggering proposals and, finally, Westminster proposed a linkage with St Thomas's and King's College. This proposal (familiarly known as the 'K.T.W. project') was finally adopted. The plan is to form a unit teaching pre-clinical medical subjects for medical students for the two Medical Schools and also paramedical subjects for B.Sc. students. The building itself would be placed geographically on the St Thomas's site. Detailed planning has been carried out on this project, and now time, permission to proceed, and money appear to be the limiting factors.

Almost simultaneously with the Todd Report, the Government published the first of several reports concerning the complete reorganisation of the administrative structure of the National Health Services! Here, for the first time the ominous word 'Area' was heard and the concept of the Area District Hospital. This enabled the retrospective historians to view with some alarm a statement made by the then Minister of Health, the Rt. Hon. Kenneth Robinson, M.P. during the Historical Symposium at the 250 Anniversary Celebrations in 1966. He said—

'However, the idea of a teaching hospital taking over a district service does not commend itself to everyone. There are those who are doubtful whether a Board of Governors would run a district service efficiently—perhaps because of the high degree of specialisation within the teaching hospital and its alleged bias towards the interesting and against the routine case, perhaps, because of the feeling that in any clash of interests a Board of Governors would give more weight to its statutory duty to the University and the teaching interest than to the needs of a balanced district service for the community. These are sincerely held doubts which will only be overcome if the undergraduate teaching hospitals make it plain to the doubters that they are as much concerned with the treatment of patients as with the teaching of medical students, and that they are prepared to see whatever modification of their traditional role is necessary to secure the provision of a full and efficient service for the local population.'

The new report proposed that the Boards of Governors of Teaching Hospitals *should be abolished*. As far as Westminster was concerned the new scheme and its modifications could not be more awkward, for the 'London division of the Group' would be in one Area and Queen Mary's Hospital in another. The position of All Saints Hospital, currently in use as a Psychiatric Hospital, and also containing the minimal care unit was similarly anomalous. The Government continued to fire further Reports on this subject; the original Green Paper was followed by a further Green Paper (sometimes called to avoid confusion the 'green and white' paper). This was followed by a White Paper and a Consultative Document. The amount of work thus thrust on the responsible officers of the Board, the Chairman of the Medical Committee, Mr

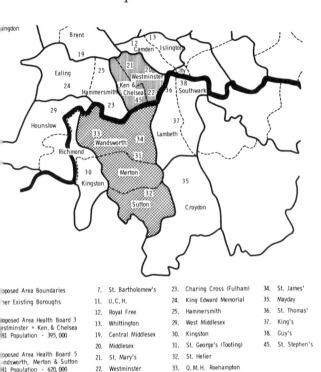

oposed Area Boundaries	7.	St. Bartholomew's	23.	Charing Cross (Fulham)	34.	St. James'
ner Existing Boroughs	11.	U.C.H.	24.	King Edward Memorial	35.	Mayday
	12.	Royal Free	25.	Hammersmith	36.	St. Thomas'
oposed Area Health Board 3	13.	Whittington	29.	West Middlesex	37.	King's
estminster + Ken. & Chelsea	19.	Central Middlesex	30.	Kingston	38.	Guy's
81 Population - 395,000	20.	Middlesex	31.	St. George's (Tooting)	45.	St. Stephen's
	21.	St. Mary's	32.	St. Helier		
oposed Area Health Board 5	22.	Westminster	33.	Q.M.H. Roehampton		
ndsworth, Merton & Sutton						
81 Population - 620,000						

Proposed Area Boundaries for Health Boards 3 and 5.

D. L. Evans and the Dean was prodigious. The upshot is that it would appear that Westminster with the Gordon and Children's Hospital will be in a District with the Chelsea and Kensington hospital manage-

ment committee. Queen Mary's Hospital will, in a special District of its own, be cut off from the huge Area, while All Saints will be 'exchanged' for the Grosvenor Hospital. Since Areas and Districts are supposed to be administratively autonomous, it would seem that the close service link between Westminster and Queen Mary's Hospital will ultimately be severed. As to the future of the teaching link this hopefully would seem to be more secure. One might add that the Administrative officers of the Board were not told what their future roles would be! As a side note, Westminster will officially be in an AH(T), i.e. Area Hospital (Teaching), which will sound strange to traditionalists and will present a problem to those desirous of encouraging the Hospital Rugby side during the Hospital cup ties! It is a sound tribute to the good sense of all members of the Group that they have endeavoured to continue their traditional roles of the care of patients and teaching throughout these perilous years.

One further major development remains to be discussed. When the Medical School was being planned in the late 1930s, anxious thoughts concerning its paltry income dominated the scene and it was decided that a branch of the Post Office could be installed in it to provide some revenue. Delay in the development caused the Post Office to be opened on a site opposite the School on the other side of Horseferry Road, while a branch of the Midland Bank was established in the School until it was removed in 1971, thus enabling the original plans of the School to be implemented. Meanwhile, in 1966 the 'Post Office site'

New Magistrate's Court building, under construction, Summer 1973.

Westminster Hospital 1716–1974

A new departure for research in Westminster was the formation of the Tumour Biology Group in 1971. This was made possible by several Research Trusts set up by generous benefactors. These include the Fane bequest in memory of the late Captain Edmund Fane, who was for many years a sufferer from Hodgkin's disease under the care of the Hospital, the Hepworth bequest by the famous sculptor Dame Barbara Hepworth, and the Lawson Trust. In addition, there is the Miriam Grenfell Research Fund for research on leukaemia set up in 1968. The Tumour Biology Group has since its foundation carried out a vigorous and co-ordinated research programme into many aspects of malignant disease and its treatment. This group is currently exploring new aspects of treatment, especially methods whereby the immunological mechanisms of the patient are exploited. In these days when students are so often the subject of public scrutiny, it is pleasant indeed to report that Westminster students are conscious of their heritage and continue to show an extremely high standard of work and efficiency. As evidence of their broadminded approach to modern living the summers of the last five years have been enlivened by 'Summer Festivals'. Here, art, music and entertainments of diverse kinds are promoted which give much pleasure to all, participants and spectators alike. This year (1973) saw the best Rugby Football side the Medical School has ever had. By brilliant and devastating attacking play they swept irresistibly into the Final of the Hospitals Cup Competition. Had not the unfortunate K. Hughes broken his collar bone the fortnight before the Final,

became ripe for development. After much discussion the Home Office decided to build a large building thereon containing a Magistrate's Court. Two of the upper floors, were, however, free. The gist of the long, tortuous, and controversial discussions was that they should form a Department of Clinical Measurement and Research, and the Department of Health agreed to finance the whole of one floor. The Board of Governors agreed to guarantee the purchase of the other floor while negotiations were being carried on with a private charitable trust. This new acquisition to the Hospital and School buildings will be (it is hoped!) completed in 1976.

A Salvo of Reports

the result one feels would have been markedly different. As it was, they were defeated by St Mary's by 20 points to 12 after a thrilling game. Time alas, brings its changes as members of the staff retire and are replaced by new members. For example, Professor N. F. Maclagan retired in September 1970 to be replaced by Professor J. Hobbs. Professor Maclagan joined the staff in 1935. Starting in two dirty rooms in the old Medical School, he built up the Department of Chemical Pathology to its present world-known eminence. His quiet, firm presence has influenced all those who have had the honour of working with him and they have gone out from Westminster to staff chemical pathology laboratories everywhere. The Author, especially, is grateful to him for his wise guidance throughout the years he has known him. Two old students must be especially mentioned here, for they have become Fellows of the Royal Society. They are Professor B. A. D. Stocker (created a Fellow in 1966) the eminent microbiologist, who is now at Stanford University, U.S.A., and Professor N. H. Ashton, created a Fellow in 1971. Professor Ashton's work in Ophthalmic Pathology is known throughout the world.

In 1970 (that Anniversary year!) the Anaesthetic Department was formally opened and called the 'Magill Department of Anaesthesia' much to the confusion of Sir Ivan himself who was forced to make a speech! *His* pupils, too, are to be found throughout the world and his successors teaching this subject are similarly well known. As one draws near to the present time it is difficult to assess the changes that take place yet they must be recorded. In 1971 for example, Putney

Putney Hospital.

Hospital (111 beds) joined the Group and is now closely linked to Queen Mary's. The year 1972 was ushered in by the award of the C.B.E. to Mr Brian Salmon, the Vice-Chairman, an award which gave us all pleasure. In 1972, St John's Battersea also became part of the Group, bringing much needed geriatric

St John's Hospital, Battersea

161

Opening of Arton Wilson House, Roehampton, February 1971.
Left to right: Sir Arton Wilson, Lord Reigate, Mr Brian Salmon, C.B.E.

beds for student and nurses' teaching and also the wise guidance of Dr L. V. Sthyr and Dr T. Howell in this most important specialty. Finally, at Roehampton, a block of residential accommodation for staff was opened by Sir Arton Wilson on April 1st 1972, a long-awaited and most valuable amenity.

The year 1973 brought a sad loss, the death of Sir

Westminster Hospital 1716–1974

Clement Price Thomas at the age of 79 on March 19th, known universally as the 'King's Surgeon' because of his successful operation on King George VI in 1951. He was of all men 'the guide, philosopher and friend' to those who had the good fortune to know and work for him. A service of Thanksgiving for his life and work was held in Westminster Abbey on May 30th and his pupil and friend Charles Drew gave a most moving eulogy. It is tragic to record also that his great contemporary Sir Stanford Cade died on September 19th. Sir Stanford's life was devoted to the diagnosis and treatment of malignant disease; his pioneer work on radium has been previously mentioned. No one who came into contact with him could fail to be influenced by his dynamic personality. The author particularly owes much to his interest and encouragement. It was a striking feature of his nature that he was much loved by his child patients and he, too, had an especial *tendresse* for them.

Finally, as the future of the School and Hospital hangs in the balance, one must mention yet another long-term plan for the future; to move lock, stock and barrel to Croydon. If our history has taught us anything, we must realise that steadiness and consistency of thought and deed have been necessary many times in the past. Let those who are to follow us remember our old motto:

Go and do thou Likewise

September 1973

162

Source Material

In writing this book the Author was most fortunate in being able to refer to the previous two histories of Westminster Hospital. These are, of course:

(1) *Westminster Hospital, an Outline of its history* (1924) W. G. Spencer (London: Henry J. Glaisler).

(2) *Westminster Hospital. Two centuries of voluntary service, 1719–1948* (1952) John Langdon-Davies (London: John Murray).

Without these two works this task would have been impossible. I have, however, taken upon myself the liberty of disagreeing with my predecessors wherever this seemed necessary.

The original sources drawn on during the writing of this book are as follows:

1. The Minutes of the Trustees and Governors of Westminster Infirmary and Hospital including the Fair Minutes of the Incurable Establishment (by kind permission of the Chairman of the Board of Governors).
2. The Proceedings of the Trustees of the Charitable Society for relieving the Sick, Poor and Needy at the Infirmary in Westminster (*see* Chapter 3).
3. Prospectuses of Westminster Medical School, 1872–1911.
4. Westminster Hospital Reports.

5. *The Broadway, Westminster Hospital Gazette,* 1899–1973.
6. *The Lancet.*
7. The *British Medical Journal.*
8. *The Dictionary of National Biography.*
9. *The Annals of the Barber-Surgeons of London* (1890) Sidney Young (London: Blades, East and Blades).
10. *The Georgian Era.* Vol. II and Vol. III, 1832–34.
11. Pettigrew's *Medical Portrait Gallery,* Vol. II, 1840.
12. *Autobiographical Recollections of the Medical Profession* (1874) James Fernandez Clarke (London: J. & A. Churchill).
13. Sir Anthony Carlisle, F.R.S. (1768–1840), R. J. Cole, B.Sc., F.R.I.C., A.M.I.Chem.E. (1952) *Annals of Science, 8,* 255–70.
14. *Things for the Surgeon. A History of the Resurrection Men* (1964) Hubert Cole (London: Heineman).
15. *William Cheselden, F.R.S.* (1953) Sir Zachary Cope, K.B., M.D., M.S., F.R.C.S. (Edinburgh & London: E. & S. Livingstone Ltd).
16. *The Letters of Charles and Mary Lamb* (1912) Ed. E. V. Lucas (London: Methuen).
17. *An Old Westminster Endowment. Being a history of the Grey Coat Hospital as recorded in the Minute Books* (1902) E. S. Day (London: Hugh Rees, 124, Pall Mall).
18. *England in the Eighteenth Century* (1950) J. H. Plumb (London: Penguin).

19. *The Age of Scandal* (1950) T. H. White (London: Penguin) No. 1839.
20. *Sir George Cayley* (1961) J. Lawrence Pritchard (London: Max Parrish).
21. *The History of Aeronautics in Great Britain* (1924) J. E. Hodgson, Limited Edition (London: Oxford University Press).
22. The Portraits of the Royal College of Physicians (1964) Gordon Wolstenholme (London: J. & A. Churchill).
23. *The Imperial Yeomanry Hospitals in South Africa* (1902) Ed. the Countess Howe. Vol. II 'Charles Stonham' (London: Arthur L. Humphreys).
24. *The Journal of the Westminster Hospital Nurses League,* 1932–73.
25. *Old and New London*, Vols. V, VII and IX (London, Paris and New York: Cassell, Petter and Galpin).
26. *The History of St George's Hospital* (1910) Part I, George C. Peachey (London: John Bale, Son and Danielsson).
27. *The Evolution of the Hospital in Britain* (1964) (Ed. F. N. L. Poynter) (London: Pitman Medical).

The Inscription on the Henry Hoare Memorial in Stourton Church

To the Pious Memory
of Henry Hoare Esq.
Son of Sir Richard Hoare sometime Lord Mayor
President of Christ's Hospital
and Member of Parliament for the City of London
His Character is too Great to be described
and yet too Good to be concealed
His Love of God and Mankind were so ardent
That he Sought all Opportunities
Honouring the One and doing Good to the Other
he was strictly pious Himself
Without being censorious of Others
Truly Humble without Affectation
Grave without Moroseness Cheerful without Levity
Just beyond Exception and Merciful without Reserve
God blessed him with a good Understanding
Which he improved by Conversing
With the best Books and wisest Men
And by a constant course of serious Meditation
He lived under a settled Habit of Private Charity
And bore a Noble Share
In all those Public acts of Piety and Mercy
Which have continued the Blessings
And averted the Judgements of God
Hence he was honoured with the Esteem of all Good Men
And with the Friendship of many the most Distinguished

by their high rank and Great Merit.
He had a well grounded and therefore inflexible Zeal
For the Faith Discipline and Worship
Of the Church of England
He gave by his last will two thousand pounds
For Erecting and Encouraging
Charity Schools and Workhouses
The profits and produce of two thousand more
To be applied yearly forever in purchasing
and giving to the Poor the Holy Bible
The Common Prayer and the whole Duty of Man
and left one thousand three hundred pounds
To other Charitable uses
His Soul went to God March 12th 1724
In the 48th year of his Age
He married Jane Daughter of Sir Willm. Benson K.C.
By Whom he had XI children two sons
and three Daughters now survive
This Monument was erected at Her expense
Being now his Mournful Widow as She was
His most faithful and Affectionate Wife.

Note: March 12th, 1724 would be March 12th, 1725 by modern reckoning. (Until 1752 the New Year began on March 25th—Lady Day).

165

Patrons and Officers of Westminster Hospital

THE PATRONS OF WESTMINSTER HOSPITAL

Augusta of Saxe-Gotha, Dowager Princess of Wales	1738–1772
Her Majesty Queen Charlotte	1772–1818
His Royal Highness The Prince Regent, later His Majesty George IV	1818–1830
His Majesty King William IV and Her Majesty Queen Adelaide	1830–1837
Her Majesty Queen Victoria	1837–1901
His Royal Highness The Prince of Wales, later His Majesty King Edward VII	1864–1910
and Her Majesty Queen Alexandra	1865–1923
His Majesty King George V	1910–1936
Her Majesty Queen Mary	1930–1954
His Majesty King George VI	1937–1952
Her Majesty Queen Elizabeth II	1952–
Her Royal Highness Princess Mary, The Princess Royal	1958–1964

THE PRESIDENTS OF WESTMINSTER HOSPITAL
(N.B. from 1719–1730 there was no President)

The Right Rev Richard Willis, DD, Lord Bishop of Winchester	1730–1734
The Right Hon. Sir Joseph Jekyll, Master of the Rolls	1734–1738
The Right Hon. the Earl of Arran	1738–1758
The Right Hon. the Earl of Lincoln	1758–1768
His Grace the Duke of Newcastle	1768–1792
The Most Noble the Marquis of Buckingham	1794–1813
His Grace the Duke of Northumberland, KG	1813–1847
His Grace the Duke of Northumberland, KG	1847–1865
The Most Noble the Marquis of Westminster, KG	1865–1870
His Grace the Duke of Westminster, KG	1870–1900
His Grace the Duke of Buccleuch, KG, KT	1900–1914
His Royal Highness the Prince of Wales, KG	1915–1936
Col. the Right Hon. Lord Wigram, GCB, GCVO, CSI	1936–1948

Appendix

Westminster Students Elected to the Staff

Surgeons

J. V. Sheldon, FRS	1786–1788
William Lynn (PRCS 1825) (Asst Surgn 1787–1788)	1788–1834
Sir Anthony Carlisle, FRS (PRCS 1828, 1837)	1793–1840
Anthony White (PRCS 1834, 1841)	1823–1849
William Bewicke Lynn (Asst Surgn 1831–1834)	1834–1853
F. Hale Thomson (Asst Surgn 1834–1843)	1843–1850
Barnard W. Holt (Asst Surgn 1846–1850)	1850–1873
George E. Legge Pearse (Asst Surgn 1869–1871)	1871–1873
Arthur Evans, OBE (Asst Surgn 1902–1919)	1919–1936
Sir Ernest Rock Carling (Asst Surgn 1906–1923)	1924–1942
Sir Stanford Cade, KBE, CB (Asst Surgn 1924–1937)	1937–1960
Sir Clement Price Thomas, KCVO (Asst Surgn 1927–1942)	1942–1958
E. Stanley Lee (Asst Surgn 1937–1948)	1948–1972
Robert Cox, MBE (Asst Surgn 1947–1948)	1948–
C. E. Drew, MVO	1951–
G. Westbury	1960–
P. H. Jones, MVO	1962–
K. P. Robinson	1968–

Specialist Surgeons

Stanley Dodd (Obstetric) (Asst Surgn 1909–1924)	1924–1937
P. D. Trevor Roper (Ophthalmic (Asst Surgn 1947–1948)	1948–
A. Briant Evans (Obstetric) (Surgeon)	1948–1972
David Evans (Orthopaedic)	1952–
E. Miles Foxen (E.N.T.)	1948–
B. G. Andrews (Orthopaedic)	1968–
H. R. M. Roberts (Obstetric)	1968–
P. M. Aichroth (Orthopaedic)	1971–

Physicians

Dr William George Maton, FRS	1801–1809
Dr John Ayrton Paris (PRCP, 1844–1856)	1809–1813
Dr William Richard Basham	1843–1877
Dr A. M. Gossage (Asst Physn 1895–1912)	1912–1918
Dr Brian Gibberd	1965–

Specialist Physicians including Anaesthetists

H. Thompson Barron (Dermatologist) (Asst Physn)	1933–1940
F. M. Allchin (Radiotherapy Dept)	1925–1956
Dr W. H. Coldwell (Radiologist) (Asst Physn 1923–1925)	1925–1945
J. A. Braxton Hicks (Pathologist)	1919–1931

Appendix

R. M. Haines (Asst Pathologist)	1937–1947	Dr C. F. Scurr, MVO } (Anaesthetists)	1950–
J. G. Humble, CVO (Haematologist)	1949–	Dr S. Feldman	1958–
P. Hansell (Medical Illustrator)	1949–	D. H. Mackenzie (Morbid Anatomist)	1958–
Dr R. Machray, CVO	1931–1968	Dr P. Cliffe (Clinical	1959–
Sir Geoffrey Organe, Professor } (Anaesthetists)	1939–	Dr J. P. Blackburn Measurement)	1969–
Dr J. B. Wyman, MBE	1948–		

3.ᵈ October 1750

*That all such Gentlemen who are
Physicians to any Branch of the Royal
Family may be a Candidate for a Physician
to this Infirmary notwithstanding any
former order*

APPENDIX D

The Hospital Prayer

The Congregation shall remain standing, and the Dean shall say:

Met together to commemorate with thanksgiving before Almighty God the inception of Westminster Hospital 250 years ago and the service to humanity which it has since performed, let us hear this Extract from the Minutes of the Hospital, wherein Mr Henry Hoare, Mr Robert Witham, Mr William Wogan and the Reverend Patrick Cockburn, met at St Dunstan's Coffee House on January 14th 1716, agreed the following proposals—

PROPOSAL No. 1
The Society proposes to provide poor sick people with necessary food and physick during illness; to procure them the advice of physicians or assistance of surgeons and to allow them nurses when necessary . . . .

PROPOSAL No. 2
As many poor honest women with child are turned out of their lodgings when near their time, the Society proposes to provide them with necessaries during lying-in, and with nurses if they have no friend or relation.

PROPOSAL No. 3
The Society proposes to visit the prisons and supply sick prisoners with such necessaries as their stock affords.

PROPOSAL No. 4
Many poor strangers from different parts of the world suffer extreme hardships; the Society proposes to relieve them and help them to return to their native country.

PROPOSAL No. 5
The Society designs to reclaim the souls of the sick. In order to do so they will procure clergymen to attend them.

Let us now give humble and hearty thanks to Almighty God, through his Son our Lord Jesus Christ who is the Great Physician of the souls and bodies of men, for the 'Charitable Proposal for Relieving the Sick and Needy and other Distressed Persons' made on this day 250 years ago which has grown into the Hospital which we know today.

After which there shall be sounded

A Fanfare of Trumpets

170

Index

Index

Index

173

Index

Index

Index

Index

Index